Also by Dominic Behan
Tell Dublin I Miss Her

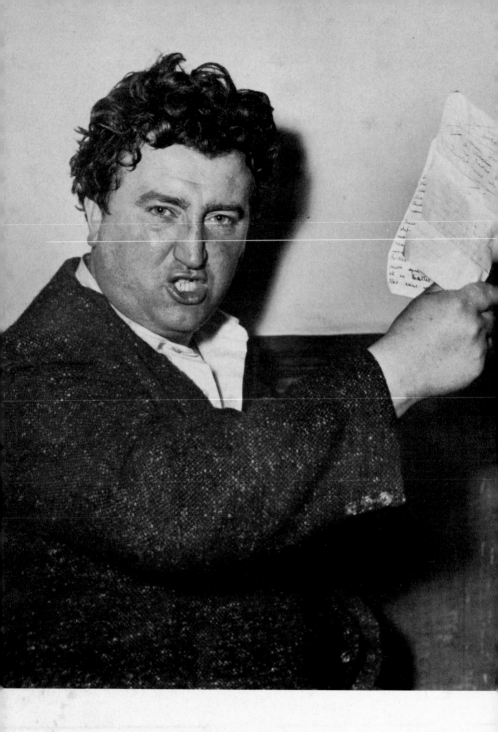

Brendan Behan

my BROTHER BRENDAN

by Dominic Behan

Simon and Schuster

New York

Introduction

BRENDAN TOLD A STORY in front of my brother Rory and I
about two years before he died. Then turning to address
Rory as he shook his fist at me he said, 'I shouldn't have said
that in front of that skinny bastard because he'll write it
down.' And a friend of ours, Eamonn Martin, told me that
Brendan accused me of having no respect for other people's
repertoires. Eamonn said it himself about me later on in a
Canadian newspaper.

I like collecting songs. I like gathering stories. It never
really worried me if they were the special preserve of somebody or other. Once a thing was not the black on the white
it became anybody's property. People are singing songs of
mine I wrote when I didn't know anything about the law of
copyright. I heard an entertainer in Manchester go right
through a script I performed at the Establishment club.
And indeed the pieces of Brendan's published by the *Irish
Press* from 1954 to 1956 were all based on people, stories of
people, and stories told by people around him. He wrote
about my father, my mother, my family, and the people
next door. And why shouldn't he? for his way of telling a
story in print was what people wanted to read. Enough said;
I am writing this book, as Brendan knew I would. If it

doesn't do him justice then I'm to blame, for my eyes and ears must have deceived me.

A person has to be trained to write a biography and even if I knew how to go about it in the accepted way it would be short and dull. Brendan Behan born 1923, jailed 1940, 1942, 1948. Published unpaid 1936, 1954; paid published work from 1954 to 1964. Made money from it from 1959 to 1964. Enjoyed the money he made from 1958 to 1961. Took a first drink at the age of seven, his last at the age of forty. Married 1955.

Excepting for two chapters in this book – the third and fourth – and the chapter in which I refer to his American visit, I was with him at all the other times I have mentioned. We went to Kerry and we drank and talked with the people I mention: Paddy Collins, Eddie Connell, Christie O'Neill, and Ena Murphy. All but the last-named are still alive. John Ryan is still alive, as is Des McNamara, Charlie Joe Gorman, Paddy Kelly, Max Sylvester, Harry Craig, and oh, many many more. And long may they continue to enjoy that state. As Brendan said in *The Quare Fella*, 'life is a damn sight better than death any day of the week'.

For obvious reasons some people appear in other clothes. A man dying at forty-one years of age is survived by his enemies as well as his friends, and libel is the most fancied meal-ticket you're likely to flash around Ireland. Every character, however, no matter how briefly dealt with, exists, or existed. It was none of my job to invent either people or what they did or said.

Lots of people are going to say 'it didn't happen this way or it didn't happen that way', 'he didn't say it one way or he didn't say it the other way'. That's bound to happen. More especially when they see how I have shifted certain locations they knew so well. I'm sorry for that, but, believe me, I'm a poor man.

People have said things about him which are just not true. For example, that he died politically disillusioned. Rubbish! The tape I quote towards the end of the book will disprove that, not to mention that Hugh McDiarmuid, the great Scots poet, was at lunch with Barbara Niven and I when Barbara told me how Brendan had just given her ten pounds for the *Worker* that same morning. It was in the summer of 1963.

He was a Republican in the Frank Ryan stamp and Ryan died from the punishment meted out to him in Franco's prisons. Brendan stood, as he said at Liverpool Assizes in 1939, for an Irish Republic of Workers and Small Farmers. If he was disillusioned it was not of the political kind. Dying, his words to Charlie Joe Gorman were, 'Don't forget the flag.'

Nobody else could have written about him as he really was but Rory or I. Because nobody else was a brother, a fellow worker, and a booser with him all three. People may come along and tell us what he was like in prison, but as he said when an old lady asked him how did Irish prisons compare with their English counterpart, 'Missus, when yeh've been to one yeh've been to them all.'

Brendan held that any man who writes a book and has to spend time introducing it shouldn't have bothered with the book. So I have confined myself to explanations not given in the text proper. What I thought of him as a brother, a man, and a writer should emerge in the reading. What he thought of me, if he in fact ever thought of me seriously, should be somewhere around too. If not, I'm going to read somebody else's book because I'm dying to know if what I've been thinking for years is right or wrong.

This is Rory's book, and I hope, brother, you like it. If so, good enough.

Dominic Behan

LONDON: 1965

1

'The winds that blow from Gardiner Street to Kimmage
Are perfumed by the knackers as they blow
And the women on the tip head picking cinders
Speak a language that the clergy do not know.'

CHILDREN'S STREET SONG

I FIRST MET HIM IN 1937 when he was fourteen and I was nine.
On the back of an ass and cart we were sitting, and it going
to Kimmage. He had an answer for everything – or so I was
led to believe. 'Why are we leaving Russell Street?' I asked.
Without looking at me he replied, 'Because me mother's
country blood is getting unsettled and she wants to get back
to the cows and cowshite.' His handsome face scowled
anger and he placed his arm around my shoulder, 'Ah, it's
not your fault, sondown.' When he was like this he would
take time with us. He had great patience in affection. Most
of the other kids in the street would get a dig from their
elder brothers for nothing, and two for anything else.
Brendan never touched me. Oh, he'd go for Seamus all
right; but me? well, 'God help yeh,' he'd say, 'but yer not
the size of threepence in coppers.' At the top of North
Great Georges Street he asked, 'Have yeh ever been here
before?' I hadn't, but I felt such an eejit because the place
was no more than a stone's throw from my granny's
tenements. 'Oh yes,' I lied, 'Charlie Mac and meself hunted
a cow up here one time.' He looked seriously to the front of
his twinkling eyes. 'Did yeh?' he asked. I felt uncomfortable

and said, 'Isn't it great to drink the milk up at the market when it's hot from the cow?' 'Don't for the love of jazes mention anything even remotely connected with farming to me again this evening,' in the middle of which I bowed my head because he had taken the Lord's name in vain. As yet I wasn't quite sure if it was the 'vein' or the 'vain', but in the religion of my mother's people yeh sort of caught on quick. Even the kids at St John of God's, who are as nutty as fruitcakes, learn the way to detect such a sinner.

As the cart turned into Parnell Street towards the monument he pointed to a great big building behind Charles Stewart Parnell and said, 'That's where I was born.' 'Yes,' I replied, 'Ma showed it to me when we were shopping here one time. How did Da go down in the world?' For a moment he looked puzzled. 'Down where?' he asked. 'Well,' I said, 'from a nice big clean house like that one to the dirty oul place where we're livin' in now.' He jumped down off the back of Mrs Farrell's cart and ran the length of O'Connell Street with my hand in his. At the tram terminus he stopped to let other people go before us and asked, 'Do you know what that place is?' I wasn't quite sure, because there was something going on in his head I didn't know about. 'Seamus says Da was born there and it was part of his grandfather's estate that was taken over from him by the British after Easter week.' He looked at me in amused astonishment. 'Are you really as much of a gobshite as yeh seem? That is the Rotunda Maternity Hospital where women go to give birth to their children.' 'They buy them there?' He flew up the stairs of the tram with a backward glance. 'Oh, Mother of jazes! And you're nine years of age.' He stared, and after a moment, seeing the tears in my eyes, he said, 'Lord God Almighty, did nobody ever tell yeh anything? What do yeh talk about with yerself and Charlie Mac and all when yer by yerselves?' So gentle, so understanding. I looked at the fond face set in the jet-black hair over a smiling set of teeth in ivory and replied, 'About the time me ma's granny was burned on a rack by the English and the farm taken for Scots settlers and how someday we'll win the lot back.' His face contorted with rage and his cheeks bulged, ready for a torrent of abuse, but all that came out was, 'Oh, for jazes' sake!' And not another word did he speak until we were well on the south side of the Liffey.

As the tramcar rumbled along around Dame Street and by the headquarters of the Irish National Painters' and Decorators' Trades Union, my brother said, 'Did yeh ever hear Da talk about the "Hall"? Well, that's it.' I leaned over his knees and peered down at the place. This was one very important building and I didn't want to miss it. I was disappointed. To me it had always been as great at least as the Bank of Ireland. My hearing of the place had built a more imposing image than the rather ordinary neo-Georgian house fronted by a gilt fascia. Da got money from this place when he was idle. Security cried out from its picture in my mind. Christmas and unemployment would never be the same again. And it seemed to me that the very next time Da went to sign on at this 'Hall' for his money that rock of sustenance, the secretary, would be gone, buried under a load of old rubbish no better than the place we were leaving and the Corporation was pulling down.

Now that Brendan had spoken first, it was safe for me to talk. 'Where's Kimmage?' I asked. 'Near the Hill of Midcain,' he replied, 'and I wouldn't be one bit surprised if we had to give three shouts when we get there.' 'Why should we have to do that, Brendan?' He smiled at my puzzled look and said, 'There were three sons of Turenn who had done a great wrong in killing an enemy, and for that they were punished by the son of him they killed. They were ordered to bring three apples from the Garden of Hesperides; the skin of the King of Greece's healing pig; the poisoned spear of Pisar; two horses and a chariot from the King of Sicily; the seven pigs of Asal; a puppy dog belonging to the King of Iruad; a cooking spit from the faery women of Finchory; and they were to give three shouts from the Hill of Midcain. All the tasks were far more dangerous than you could think.' 'Did they do them?' 'They did,' he replied, 'and got killed for their trouble.' 'Oh Lord!' I thought.

At the top of Clanbrassil Street, by the junction of the South Circular Road, I saw Rory, my eldest brother, sitting beside Seamus on the front of a horse-drawn cart. Ma's furniture was piled precariously on the float, pinnacled by the horse-hair sofa through which the strong stuffing protruded with cutting edge. Da had been going to mend it for as long as I could remember; he had thought about it a great deal. Just now, as it wagged from side to side, it seemed all Da's worries would soon be over. 'Brendan,' I said, 'there's Rory with the things for the new house. And if they don't stop and tie up the load that sofa will fall off.' He looked along the line of my pointing finger with little interest and said, 'It will that,' and it seemed to me that he would have derived immense satisfaction from such an occurrence.

At the military barracks taken over from the British in 1922, and named after Arthur Griffiths, Brendan said, 'Did yeh ever hear Ma talkin' about the man who wrote *Twenty Men from Dublin Town*?' I did, but whenever Brendan began like that we knew that the question would be rhetorical, so I said nothing. 'Well, that place there is called after him.' 'Was he the one who was shot with Michael Collins?' I asked. 'How did yeh know about things like that? He was a close friend of Collins' but he wasn't shot. He died before Collins – overworked, Ma said. Though she also said that to her it was obvious Collins himself knew he wouldn't be long after Griffiths.' 'How could she know that?' I asked. 'She was behind him at Griffiths' funeral and all the time Collins kept looking over his shoulder.' 'What was he like, Brendan, Collins I mean?' 'I can't say personally, because I wasn't born at the time of his death, but, according to Father O'Flanagan, Collins was a good man, and that's alright by me.' 'Bernard Keegan's mother said Father O'Flanagan was in favour of those people in Spain. And would be unfrocked.' 'Well,' said Brendan, 'if he's unfrocked twenty times a day it won't be half as many times as Bernard Keegan's mother.'

Kids were playing under a street-lamp by the tram-stop at Sally's Bridge. 'P'liceman, p'liceman, don't take me. Take that boy behind the tree. He took silver, he took gold, p'liceman, p'liceman, please take hold.' Very grand songs. Very grand kids and not one of them but had trousers and coats to match. Indeed most of them had school caps. Where we lived in Russell Street it was, 'Limpy Dan, Limpy Dan, lift yer leg and yeh'll see a wee man.' This place appealed to me, for I'd always had a yearning for nice clothes and people who spoke well, who came home on trains at the end of mysterious times called 'terms'. The *Hotspur* comic was full of great things, like schools with places 'out of bounds' and 'tuck' shops. Maybe it was all true after all. 'Is the whole of Kimmage like this?' I asked. 'Kimmage!' said Brendan indignantly, 'Kimmage! Would yeh for God's sake look at the size of the houses. Shabby genteel maybe. But big. Closed Hall doors, but enough to keep a body warm for a few hours if chopped up nicely. Grass enough at the front but nothin' a few bags of sand and cement couldn't very quickly eradicate. Yer still in some sort of civilisation. Those kids singin' out there are the last yeh'll ever hear, because the chisellers in Kimmage don't have time to play games, they have to go huntin' with their fathers. Take it from me, sondown, we're on our way to the wild west.'

Brendan sat, staring, sightless, as the long circular snake slipped southwards. He sighed. My heart was filled with a sense of adventure, but all he had ever wanted was behind him: the smell of Mountjoy Brewery, the roar from Croke Park Stadium, the sound of 'city' cattle on their way to the docks down the North Circular Road. The view from Granny's grandstand window of a street teeming with life. Even the smell of Mrs Cullen's pigs in the lane.

It was dark and with the sky for a roof the top of the tram was very cold. 'Could we go downstairs, Brendan?' I asked. 'It's not worth it now, Dom,' he said. 'We'll soon be in Dolphin's Barn.' 'Is that near Kimmage?' 'Well,' he thought for a moment, 'to be quite honest I don't know where it really is, though I passed it one time in a cab with me granny. They used to come out here durin' the summer-time, me granny and her friends. Out to *The Red Cow* in Clondalkin, or maybe the *Cuckoo's Nest* near Tallaght or *Lena Delaney's* in Bohernbreena, *Kennedy's* of Old Bawn, or to the pub of many names in Rathcool. Then back into the cab stocious drunk while the driver unable to do anything about it would let the horse steam back to Dublin. Then she'd lift me out of the cab and explain to the neighbours how "we've just had a lovely day in the country, messrs., and of course the air is too strong for poor Bren". I've often inhaled more air in a picture house.' He laughed at what he had just said and then sat back, his head turned away from me. Granny was on his mind now. His granny and nobody else's. She had died some few months before and her act he construed as some sort of betrayal. He had lived by her and with her. He slept in our place but that was about all. A lot of his life died when she did, for his granny was everything

14

in the world to him. 'Poor little Bren,' she would say, 'loves his gran.' His granny had never much time for me, Rory and Sean were greeted civilly enough, Seamus she couldn't stand since he was named after her first husband, our grandfather. In later times I wrote about his granny in a somewhat critical way and Brendan never forgave me. But, then, it was only after he had refused forgiveness for a million other real and imaginary wrongs perpetrated against him by a brother who was always 'a bit of a gobshite'.

We came to a junction of village size and the conductor cried, 'Dolphin's Barn! All off here!'

We gained the foot of the stairs in time to see the driver and conductor slip around the corner on the north side of Dolphin's Barn. Brendan swore and muttered, 'Jazes, I wanted to ask him about a bus goin' out to this kip. Ah, they won't be long anyway; probably just gone for a pint.' He looked down at me and with a smile said, 'Go across to that place with the light on and ask them where the sheriff is. We should report to him at once, I'm sure.' I was halfway across the road when he called, 'Will yeh come back out of that, yeh thick, before one of these country eejits captures yeh for a leprechaun!' I didn't like people making fun of my height, so I crossed back to him and sat sullen with bowed head on the corner of the kerb. He put his arm around me and I shook it away. He asked me did I want to hear about Fiann Macool, and though I would have loved to have the story of Ireland's legendary hero related I just turned my head further away. 'Alright,' he said, 'keep yer anger in and me out. But yeh'll want me company when we have to leave here and walk into the night.'

Although 'Dolphin's Barn' was connected to the city by an unbroken stream of streets and houses it had lost none of its village characteristics. The tallest house in it would not have come up to the chest of one of our Georgian slums. There was no sound of singing children here, and people passing went by and spoke to each other with a touch of that 'God Bless all Here Irish', and the Catholic chapel surveyed the scene with evident satisfaction. It was then – and, I suppose, it still is – three and one half miles from Dublin. The driver and conductor came across the road and Brendan said, 'We're tryin' to get to Kimmage, please.' 'Out there over the bridge,' replied the driver. 'But we want to get a bus,' said Brendan, as the driver got on to his tram. He looked at Brendan and unlocked his lever and contemplated the glass in front. The conductor straightened his bag, pulled the bell strap, said, 'A bus! To Siberia!', and as the tram sped away, retracing its steps, the conductor's loud laughter could be heard singing in the distance.

2

'Some day I'll go back again to Kimmage
Be it only at the closing of my mind
To see the little children beat their grannies
Or tripping up the crippled and the blind.'

WE CUT ACROSS a canal bridge and along the main Crumlin Road, which was very dimly lit. The houses on either side could have been part of a ghost-town set, for all the life was in them. But if Crumlin Road was dark it was like Piccadilly Circus compared to the road running westward along the Lorette Convent. In a stream of his own invective Brendan fell into a hole and muttered, 'Well, me mother will be as happy as Larry out here, but thank God me granny is buried in consecrated ground! Can you imagine it? Me canvassin' for Fianna Fail in '32. Just think of it! At nine years of age there I was out gettin' pennies and two-pences for the party machine. For what? So that they could put the whole of Dublin out into a bog. They could've built flats in the centre of the town for us and kept reservations like this for them that come in from the country. Home from home, it would have been. But us! And the only grass we ever saw we were asked to keep off it. Is that a light?' I saw a row of paraffin lamps flickering some two hundred yards away. And as we made for their red glow the moon forced her way through the blanket of cloud and lit up the strangest scene. We were

17

in the middle of skeletoned houses, untiled roofs, unplastered walls, unglazed windows. 'Oh, Mother of the devine God!' said Brendan, 'and to think that last year me mother burned me instructions that would have taken me to Spain. Afraid I would have been hurt. Well, I can safely say I'd rather have been shot outside Madrid with the friends I know than die out in this kip alone!'

The oil lamps were appointed around a glowing coke brazier guarding the entrance to a watchman's hut. A little old man, who looked as though he had seen as much of life as any of us are likely to see, sat in the back of the hut grasping a shifting spanner in his frightened hand. He jumped as Brendan approached.

'Excuse me,' said my brother, 'but we're looking for Kildare Road.' 'I couldn't say,' feebled the old man. 'It could be anywhere. They leave me here at seven in the evenin' and come back at seven in the mornin'. And durin' that time I put neither heel nor toe outside the front of this hut.' Brendan laughed in spite of himself and asked, 'And supposin' somebody comes along and pinches half the buildin' materials?' 'It's none of me business, young fella. If they were to come along and leave the place naked – and, mind yeh, they do regularly – so long as they don't come near me I'm quite happy. D'ye know there hasn't been sight nor light of a polisman in this place since the buildin's started to go up. In the summer it was as hard to find where yeh lived as it is now. No names on the roads. Houses with no numbers. I hope yeh find wherever it is yer goin' but,' he lowered his voice to a whisper, 'if I was youse I'd turn back before it's too late.' Brendan said, 'Good night,' we walked a couple of yards, he turned back, crept to the side of the hut and started wailing like a banshee through the canvas. The old man's head appeared furtively round the opening, only to be greeted by an unmercifully blood-curdling scream from Brendan. Shaking like a leaf, the old man shook his fist at Brendan and cried, 'The cursea jazes on yeh, anyway!' Brendan roared with laughter and narrowly missed falling into another hole. 'Well,' said he, 'isn't that a comical oul fucker altogether. He's supposed to have them lamps around those holes and instead he has his own little tabernacle floodlit. Ah sure I dare say he's right.' I'd never heard Brendan use what we called 'real swear' words before and now for the first time this invective made me jump a bit, so I apologised to God and sneakingly reminded Him that if He had some reason to leave Brendan in this forsaken spot He'd certainly nothing on me. Anyway, I was only nine. Brendan was fourteen and God should know that.

We had run laughing, or Brendan laughing and I forced, about a quarter of a mile and Brendan stopped to hold his hands around his stomach with his face wreathed in smiles and his chest heaving. 'D'yeh know,' he asked, 'what's goin' to beat Banagher?' he asked and answered, 'Me father! Me poor oulfella, he thinks we're still in Russell Street! Now he'll go back there and stay in Gill's until closing time. Then out he comes, gets up on his bike fluthered drunk and like a paralytic on a tightrope he makes his way out here. Well, honest to Christ, it's bad enough for them as can see! I lay the odds he winds up in that little watchman's confession box. Well, Kimmage me love, tonight thou shalt be consecrated, by jazes thou shalt!'

The moon went back to bed and darkness rose again in silence. Brendan gripped my hand firmly and urged me to hold the crown of the concrete road. Suddenly the night below was lit by a lamp travelling horizontally and swinging to the accompaniment of trundling wheels while horses' hooves drew silver sparks in a trotting row. 'Begod,' said Brendan, 'there's a turnin' there a bit to our right. Get a move on and we'll follow the brave path ploughed by that decent homesteader.' We turned the corner and were greeted by a sign in a garden bearing the legend 'Clogher Road'. 'Well,' said Brendan, 'isn't that a curse? The one road we know in the whole of Kimmage and it's not our own. Eh, wait, though, there's a family moving in there. If they can't tell us where we want, they might give us a cup of tea.' We made our way to a house with an opened hall door through which light flooded. On the road outside stood a patient horse harnessed to a chained dray. On the roadway around the horse and cart were scattered odds and ends of furniture. 'Lift up one of them chairs,' said Brendan, 'and I'll carry up this table.' We brought up the pieces of furniture to the hall door and just then an old man emerged. 'What are yis doin' with me things?' he demanded. Brendan saluted smartly, and said, 'Just helping you move in, sir.' 'Well, blast yeh anyway,' said the old man, 'it's taking me wife and I all our time to move out.'

Brendan shook with laughter and asked, 'Movin' out, mister?' 'Movin' out,' said the old man defiantly, and an old woman joined him, shook a warning finger at Brendan, and said, 'And no one is goin' to stop us!' 'Missus,' said Brendan, 'I think yeh show the best of good sense. All we want to know is the way to Kildare Road.' They told us that our place would branch off as a continuation of the road she was leaving. We restored the furniture we had moved to its place on the road, and as we took our leave of the home-sick exiles the old woman whispered to her husband, 'Ah, musha, God love them, and they so young. And mind yeh, Mick, a child's mind is easily scarred.'

Seventy Kildare Road is part of a two-house block, both of which houses together would hardly make a sweating room for a second-class Turkish baths. And yet it was supposed to be one of the more superior dwellings for which the Corporation charged an extra two and sixpence per week. It had, of course, a separate bathroom, that is not to say that it was apart from the toilet, it merely meant that in the seven-and-sixpenny model the bathroom was combined with the kitchen; and an added feature in the cheaper house was the novelty of passing through the Kit/Bth to get to the toilet, which was located on the other side. Somebody told me that the man responsible for their design committed suicide. I'm quite sure his death, if at all, was accidental, for no man with a mind like his could ever succeed in anything so calculated as taking a life, even his own.

Brendan had been given the keys by my mother and we were to light fires that the house be well aired when Rory arrived with the furniture. 'Oh God,' he said, 'I forgot to get some candles. Look, Dom, slip across to one of those houses and see would they give yeh the loan of a stub. They're bound to have bulbs for the electric light by this time and they won't be needin' candles anyway.'

I must have been at least five minutes saying, 'Excuse me, please, but I was wondering if yeh could . . .' While a voice from inside kept shouting, 'What is it? Who are yeh? What d'ye want? I'm sorry but we're gone to bed.' Brendan shouted over to know what in the name of God was keeping me. I crossed the road and said, 'I couldn't make much sense out of that. There's some man in there keeps callin' out but he won't open up the door.' 'I don't blame him,' said Brendan, 'in a place like this. Christ, I'm sure they eat their dead out here.' 'I think that's Mr Reddin, over in that house, Brendan. It sounded a bit like his voice.' 'Who? Yeh mean oul Cruk?' He twisted his upper lip and pushed it against his nose as he did when doubtful. 'Ah,' he said, 'I hardly think so. I think most of the people on our side of Russell Street were split up. The Corporation seldom leave old neighbours together. Still, we might as well find out. Come on over.'

As we reached the garden wall of the house in question we heard a woman's voice shouting, 'Will yeh come up to bed? Cruk, will yeh for jazes' sake leave them pigeons alone an' come up to bed?' 'Begod,' said Brendan, 'yer right, it's the Cruk himself and his loved one, the only woman Sailor Clancy ever told to go and fight her match.' Brendan knocked for a few minutes and then Mr Reddin spoke from the back of the door, 'What is it? Who is it?' 'It's me, Mr Reddin,' answered Brendan. 'Who? Who is me?' 'It's Brendan Behan.' 'Ah, yis can't cett me like that. There's no Brendan Behan out here. Brendan Behan is in Russell Street. All the Behans is in Russell Street. Sensible decent people. All in Russell Street.' 'But I am Brendan Behan, Mr Reddin.' 'Well, then, if yeh are Brendan Behan,' he asked, 'tell me what the chisellers in Russell Street used to shout.' Brendan whispered to me that he wouldn't be able to shout for laughing, so I cried, 'Idybanoyocks!'

Brendan looked on me as though staring at a fool at a fair and though he and Terry House and a lot more had been in the habit of shouting that meaningless cry to the annoyance of many a neighbour, just now I felt a proper idiot. First the top bolt of the hall door rattled, then the second, all was needed then, a good stout pull from a strong hand and the native Irish timber was forced from between the door-jambs. Mr Reddin greeted us like somebody might welcome a long-lost relative on seeing him for the first time in the Klondike. It was hard to believe that the Reddins had moved only three weeks before. He came towards Brendan with two hands outstretched and in both he grasped one of my brother's, pulling him inside as he walked backwards. 'Well, there yeh are. Young Brendan. Well, yer a sight for sore eyes. What are yis doin' out in this oul place? Yeh hardly came out to see us.' He stopped abruptly and unbelieving said, 'Yis haven't left?'

Then, laughing at the stupidity of the suggestion, he went on, 'Ah, no. Ah God no. The Dublin Corporation may be all powerful where some folk are concerned but their authority means nothin' to yer father. There's the man for them! "Jack Reddin", says he – never called me nothin' but Jack – "Jack," he says, "a Dublin man should go to live in the country when he can do nothing else. I know I'll have to move there somethime but I'll know not a haporth about it because I'll be gettin' carried to me six be four." ' 'He doesn't know anything about it,' said Brendan, as Mrs Reddin, looking as surly and as Dublin dealerish as I'd ever seen her, proceeded her inquisitive descent from the top of the stairs. Cruk, ashen-faced, said, 'Yeh don't mean to tell me yer poor father is . . . Ah, God be good to him. The heart of the roll! I remember the time . . .' Brendan interrupted to say, 'Oh there's not a bother on me father, Mr. Reddin.' 'But I thought yeh said . . .' Cruk began. 'I only said he knows nothing about us moving out here,' said Brendan.

On seeing Mrs Reddin, my brother extended a smile and a hand. The hand she ignored, the smile she froze, and in a voice like pound notes she demanded, 'Well? What is it yis want now? Is it a lend of a cup of sugar? Or maybe a cup of tea?' 'Ah now, love,' said gentle Cruk to his ogre. 'Ah now don't be goin' on like that, love. Sure isn't it nice to say hello to an oul neighbour.' Mrs Reddin would hear none of it. 'Say hello,' she muttered. 'If they're near our door they're lookin' for somethin'. I've always said that if one sinner soul comes near from Russell Street he'll be lookin' for somethin'. Don't keep them in the hall anyway, Cruk; if the neighbours hear us they might think *I* owe *them* somethin'. Come in to the kitchen.' The kitchen was off the hall and the difference between the two was that one had a sink and a gas cooker. Dolls' houses made by dwarfs with Lilliputians in mind.

Mrs Reddin ordered Cruk to brew a pot of tea. 'And not too strong, mind yeh. Think sometimes, bejazes, he was some sort of an Indian farmer.' For the first time Cruk revolted – well, paused in retreat – 'Ah, don't take the Lord's name in front of Carmel, love.' Carmel! I was raging. She was my young sister. 'Dominic,' said Brendan to Cruk, but accidentally his words met Mrs Reddin. She put her hand to her head, and said, 'Don't tell me about the little gett!' She glared at me and showed me the back of her hand, so that I moved nearer the shelter of Brendan. 'If I'd a got yeh, the day yeh locked that lavatory door when yeh saw me come burstin' down the stairs . . .' Brendan put his hand to his mouth and pretended to cough, but there was nothing he could do about his eyes. 'An' yerself, that's the little saint,' she mimicked Brendan's granny, ' "poor gentle Bren". I won't forget the time yeh put the shite on me gramophone record an' it went flyin' around me lovely room. Be the lord jazes!' Brendan moved back and kept me between him and Mrs Reddin.

Cruk prepared to pour tea in willow-patterned china. Mrs Reddin lifted them from under the spout of the pot and put four delft cups in their place. 'Them, is for visitors an' I'll tell yeh no more,' she grunted. With a sort of quiet dignity Mr Reddin said, 'Sure the white ones hold a drop more, boys,' and in the same soft voice he asked, 'and what was it yeh were sayin' about yer father knowin' nothin' about the movin'? Surely yer mother wouldn't defy the authority of the man of the house.' 'He doesn't know we're here, anyway,' said Brendan. 'Well, good Lord,' said Cruk, 'after the grand stand he made. A man of principle – wasn't I sayin' that to yerself love, just this . . .?' 'Principle, how are yeh!' cried the irritable Mrs Reddin; 'too bloody lazy to put his arse out of joint by movin'.' Cruk interrupted, 'Was it rainin' when yis were leavin'?' 'No, Mr Reddin,' said

Brendan, 'it was fine.' 'Were yis the last in the street or was it the Knights?' 'We were the last,' Brendan replied. 'Mrs Knight went last week with her daughter.' 'Ah, and what part of the new scheme did they put her?' asked Mr Reddin. 'She didn't go to the scheme,' said Brendan, 'I hear she got a place in Rathmines.' 'Rathmines.' Mr Reddin was pleasantly surprised. 'Well now, isn't that nice for her. And well deserved. A most respectable little woman tryin' to bring up a daughter on her own. And she's done well to find a place in a nice area like Rathmines.' 'What the hell are yeh talkin' about?' demanded his wife. 'Out to a cheap room in another tenement because she couldn't afford the high rents in Kimmage. Their likes shouldn't be let come out here. And just as lucky for them, because if they paid it twice the police would be up to know where they got it!' 'Ah now, love,' began Cruk, 'that's no way to speak about decent old neighbours.' 'Neighbours!' she began. 'Decent! Respectable! They were about as respectable as me arse in a hurry!'

'Now, love, I remember Stephen Behan and——' began Cruk again. His wife was on the subject like a flash. 'Stephen Behan! I remember when he was let out of prison with all them other IRA men after the treaty. With a big red beard flowing like a demon he dashed up the stairs and caught poor Mr Costigan in the bed and cried like a lunatic as he lifted him up to smash him on the door, "Are you the dirty bastard that's bein' makin' my wife's life a hell while I've been away?" And with that he flung that young man from the top to the bottom of 14 Russell Street. Poor Mr Costigan, he's walked with a limp ever since. And him a pipe major in a band. And yeh forget the time I suppose,' she glared at Cruk, 'that he came up and threw me new gramophone out the window because I wouldn't turn it off when he said he had a sick child below. And when I sent you down to

challenge him in the middle of the street he made a laughin'
stock of yeh by tellin' yeh in front of everybody to go back
and get your wife.' 'Ah now,' said Cruk, 'Stephen was a——'
'A savage,' supplied Mrs Reddin. 'Lord Almighty and to
think of it. He was nearly a Jesuit. Al Caponey in a collar.'
She stopped ranting for a split second, barely long enough
for us to hear the flat Dublin voice of my brother Seamus
singin', 'Holy Moses, I am dyin', send for the doctor before
I die. The cat is sittin' in the coal hole, so shove a poker up
it's ... Holy Moses, I am dyin' ' on *ad finitum*.

'Sweet God!' groaned Mrs Reddin, 'there they come.
Out of the darkness to hide their poverty.' Then, creasing
her face into the suggestion of a smile, she said quietly, 'I
suppose yer mother will be along soon with the rest. That's
why she waited, wasn't it?' 'Waited for what, Mrs Reddin?'
asked Brendan. 'The odds and ends,' she replied confidentially, 'that'd be left there when everybody else had gone.
Seein' as she'd be the last in the street like.' 'The odds and
ends of what, Mrs Reddin?' asked my brother.

'Well, eh, yeh know what I mean like,' her simulation of
confidence was the personification of low cunning, 'there'll
be a lot of lead in them oul houses, and sure, where will that
all go? Brass water taps and lead pipin', them is valuable.
An', of course, there'd be lead on the roof-tops.' Cruk
interrupted, 'But sure his mother'd hardly be able to climb
up on the roof of the house, love.' His wife turned on him
angrily, 'It's not his mother I'm talkin' about. Wouldn't
Stephen do it and it his job climbin' big ladders.' Brendan
grinned and said, 'If he can even see a hole in a ladder this
minit I'll be surprised. And as for climbing roof-tops I
imagine it'll take him all his time to climb on to his bike.'
He was tired of all this now and quietly but efficiently took
command of the situation. 'The houses belong to the
Dublin Corporation, who retain the right to acquire all

that remains of them. If they were still the property of anybody in my family it would be my Uncle Paddy. As for my father, Mrs Reddin, he's a first-class tradesman. Painters and decorators of his standing are not in the habit of dealing in rags and bones. And now, Mr Reddin,' he ended grandly, 'thank you, sir, and your good wife for your hospitality.' And outside he roared with laughter as he dashed across the road to where Rory was waiting with the furniture and Seamus still singing, 'Holy Moses, I am dyin'.

'Where in the namea God you been?' said Rory as Brendan approached, and in the same breath he turned to Seamus and whispered, 'Will yeh for Christ's sake stop. Me mother is comin' up the street behind yeh and if she hears yeh singin' that it's me that'll get into trouble not you.' 'Hello, Ma,' shouted Brendan, 'we got here.' 'I can see that,' she replied, dragging Carmel wearily behind her, 'and I'm half murdered tryin' to find it.' Rory stopped in the act of loosening the ropes and muttered to Brendan, 'Jazes! It can't be. God it is! Hello, Mrs Reddin!'

'There yeh are, love,' said Mrs Reddin, 'and yerself, Mrs Behan. Well, isn't grand to see an oul neighbour. I was just sayin' to John, "Cruk", says I, "isn't grand to have an oul neighbour comin' to live near us. Like oul times." Now, mam, if there's e'r a thing yeh'd be wantin' yeh've only to ask. Anything I can do at all to help yeh move in. Cruk,' she shouted across to her husband, 'will yeh come over outa that and help an oul neighbour in. I can lend yeh bulbs an' things if yis wantin' them, mam, because it's the 'lectric out here yeh know. Anything yeh want as I've said before. Cruk! Will yeh for God's sake come over!' Ma coldly but politely said, 'Thank yeh, mam. But I'm sure I've all I want.' And with that she turned into the house and, following Brendan, closed the hall door behind her without a backward glance. We were in 70 Kildare Road, Kimmage.

3

'Two foreign old monarchs in battle did join
Both wanting their heads on the back of a coin
If the Irish had sense they'd drown both in the Boyne
And Partition throw into the ocean.

  The Sea, oh the Sea is the gradh geal mo croide
  Long may it stay between England and me
  It's a sure guarantee that some hour we'll be free
  Thank God we're surrounded by water.'

DA CAME HOME FROM WORK, left his bike at the corner of the
house, and I scooted it round to the back. He looked at the
weeds growing high in the garden and laughed. 'Yeh know,'
he said, 'in the famine times people would have been
delighted to take a bag of those and boil them.'

'I wonder how they tasted,' I asked.

'Like weeds that have been boiled, I'd imagine.'

Brendan came whistling up the path and Da said,
'C'mere; I want just a word with you.'

'What's that, Da?' asked Brendan.

'What were you up to today?'

Brendan with a half-smile and blushing look said, 'Well
I . . .'

'I know yeh weren't in Tech because only tonight I met
Charlie O'Byrne and he nearly died of shock on account
you told him that yeh were takin' the day off because of

my death.' I was shocked. Fancy anybody making up a thing like that about their father – or even their mother. Brendan was embarrassed. 'I didn't mean it, Da,' he began, 'it was a sort of a joke. A poor one, I admit, but at the time I didn't think of it in bad taste. I'm sorry.'

'It doesn't interest me, Brendan. It doesn't interest me one little bit even if yeh told your teacher I was bloody well cremated. What does worry me is why you did it.'

'I told yeh,' said Brendan irritably, 'it was a bloody joke. Now surely we can drop the whole bastardin' subject.' Da ignored Brendan's anger and said, 'Before we go inside to where yer mother is I want to know how you spent the time you took off.' He was getting into a temper now, the sort where he sat and boiled. He wouldn't beat us, for he didn't believe a child was a match for a man and that was an end to corporal punishment. 'What I do with my time is my own,' replied Brendan.

'Not,' said my father, 'if it concerns me.'

'What do you mean, concern you?' demanded Brendan. 'How could anything I do concern you?'

'I'll tell you,' said Da, 'if you were in Killiney Castle today where they're makin' the stuff for the English campaign that concerns me.'

Brendan looked surprised. 'How d'ye know about Killiney?' he asked.

'That doesn't matter,' said Da, 'what matters is that I don't agree with this campaign in England.'

'So?' asked Brendan sullenly.

'So,' my father replied, 'under no circumstances are you to make 70 Kildare Road one of the jumpin'-off grounds for it.'

'Same as all the other Staters,' muttered Brendan, and Da heard him. He went white with temper and I could see the knuckles sticking through the taut skin on his hands.

'Don't you dare call me a Stater. I fought against the murder gang before yeh were born. I was in jail – their bloody jail – *when* yeh were born. If you're ever *half* the Republican I was you'll be damned lucky.' And as if by some prearranged signal they both turned in their own circles and walked, Da into the house where Ma was waiting and Brendan down to the pub where somebody was waiting for him.

'Strange people,' I thought, 'let's hope to God they don't start arguing tonight during "Band Wagon".'

They have a saying in Dublin, 'Yer better off idle than walkin' about'. So far as I can discover, Brendan got two things from attending Mr O'Byrne's painting class at Bolton Street Technical School: enough knowledge of signwriting to enable him to write a fascia for a Parisian restaurateur which read: 'There is but one Au Fait Café in Paris and this is fucking well it.' And it got him away from Kimmage and back to the land he was fighting for – North Dublin. He was as well off walking around Liverpool with a suitcase full of stuff as being idle on the ratepayers of Dublin at fifteen shillings a week which he never brought home anyway. Though I do remember how Ma used to commiserate with him every time he lost his wages – each week. 'Poor Brendan,' she'd say, 'still, yeh have your health. Thank God!'

My Granny Furlong (Rory and Sean's grandmother by a previous marriage of my mother) was the first of the family to be knocked off in the campaign. Herself and my two aunts, Emily and Evelyn, were caught when they went to England to set up house for those on active service. Granny was over seventy and the courts might easily have let her back to Ireland to end her days in peace. Still, we've learned not to expect a hell of a lot of forgiveness whenever we're caught trying to chop six inches off John Bull's tail. Johnny wasn't too bad about it and let them off with a caution and seven years apiece.

Around that time, apart from listening to BBC, I was a member of Na Fianna Eireann and my O/C was a chap called John O'Hagen, who lives with me nowadays whenever he visits the land of the oppressor. On his last visit he saw I was working on this book and asked, 'But can you tell us what your brother was up to before he joined the campaign?' I could and did, because I had been doing a broadcast in the North of England some years ago and while I was waiting to hear if what they call the 'Takes' were alright I drank a while with a Belfast Protestant by the name of Tom McKevitt. The only reason I mention he is a Protestant is because it has to do with the story.

When you talk to a chap like McKevitt you begin to realise that despite the separate thinking of some folk, the border separating the north-east and the rest of Ireland is something kept alive by suggestion. It exists by virtue of the two governments of Ireland. And, I suppose, radio, TV, and the Press play a part. It cannot be felt, smelled, or tripped over. It cannot be seen by the naked eye even when the naked eye is wearing a microscope. It is an equatorial or subliminal division, a physical illusion but an economic reality which leaves twenty-six of the counties of Ireland where they have been since when ever the world was first made and six more under the eventual jurisdiction of Westminster. At first sight I thought McKevitt was an Orangeman. One of those strange people who think of Republicans as being synonymous with the Roman Catholic whom they see as ever ready to drag the country away and stick it somewhere in the heel of the Italian boot. They, the Orangemen, that is, want us to hold the fort for the Crown in memory of William of Orange. Now that's all the politics I'm going to give you because it becomes twice as confusing

The young Behans: back row, Seamus, Dominic, Brendan and Brian; front row, Carmel (right) and friend.

Brendan in trouble—barred from a London theatre.

Brendan, with Mrs D. McNamara and Mrs P. Walsh.

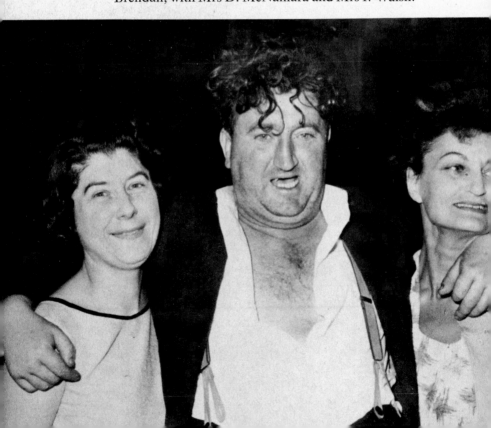

when I tell you how the Crown in question belongs to England and King William was a Dutchman.

'No, I'm not an Orangeman,' said McKevitt. 'A Protestant alright, and so were a good many fine rebels, Wolfe Tone, Robert Emmet, to mention a couple.' I could have gone one better and reminded him that Yeats, Shaw, Swift, and Goldsmith, not to mention O'Casey, were also Protestant. He didn't, I'm sure, need reminding, for as he carried on with his story I could see that he was as well read and informed as the next man. 'I'm about ages with your brother,' he continued, 'maybe a year or so younger. In '38 I lived in Ton Street, the Catholic part of the Falls.'

'I thought all the Falls Road was more or less Catholic.'

McKevitt grinned and said, 'I'd say more than less.

'My family moved to the Falls before I was born. By God, many's the time I laughed at the notions of grandeur your crowd associated with all Protestants. During the depression my family, and this is as true as I'm sitting here tonight, were actually so poor that we were forced to sell the saucepans off the stove. Since there wasn't anything to go into them I don't suppose it made such a hell of a lot of difference. For about three years the old man didn't earn as much as would keep an old-age pensioner for a week, let alone what would nourish a wife and child. Rickets!' snarled McKevitt, 'I could tell them about rickets. And crawling as a child of four to a cupboard and finding nothing but the smell of soap. God, Irish women are diabolical for the carbolic. They used to have a notice down in the Yards: "No Catholics! No Popery!" My old man wrote underneath it: "Or Jews! Or Christianity!" "Or Prods! Or Billies!" The Lodge crowd laughed at it then because there was no work for anybody, but they remembered my father later when things were moving at the Yards. I think he must have been the last man back that wasn't a Catholic.

'Anyway, I was saying about us and the Falls. We were surrounded by Catholics, but none of us ever thought much about religion, we were neighbours. We kids queued for soup from the same charity pot. Our fathers drew dole from the same exchange. Prod or Pape yeh starved, and it was the same hungry feeling. Then after a while the drums rolled again and the pogroms started. I hope to God yeh never witness the like, Dominic. Rushing around like wild things, smashed everything Papish or belonging to a Pape. I saw a crowd of lunatics singing "Abide With Me" as they trampled on statues of the crucifixion in a Catholic repository. And don't let anyone ever tell me that hymns have an inner beauty all their own. The way this crowd sang them they could have been chanting the "Horst Wessel".

'One night I came home and found my father and mother in the street and on a handcart they had whatever had been inside the house. They'd so much gear that after putting everything they owned on there was room for anyone else's stuff who happened to be going their way. They'd a big mattress for themselves and a little one stuffed with straw that I used to sleep on. By God, I wasn't sorry to see the end of that heap of crap because it used to have a habit of gathering in little lumps beneath me in the most awkward places. On top of this was a table, two chairs, and a couple of other things – I can't remember precisely what.

'I can remember, however, that there were two young men there, your brother and another. The other fellow would have been about eighteen or nineteen. Each had a gun as big, I think, as a cannon, though I suppose they were really the ordinary size, whatever that might be. My father and mother stood facing them and I felt sick because I felt pity for the old man. Jesus! it's the most terrible feeling.

'My father argued with them. Mother, of course, pleaded with them. It didn't do any good. They had orders to throw

34

every Protestant family out of our quarter and that's what they were going to do. Can you imagine it? All our neighbours hiding behind their curtains and not one of them to say stop. Anyway, my father got fed up with my mother's begging and said, "Come on, Isobel" – there's a real oul Scots planter name for you now – "we'll go somewhere else." "But," asked the sensible woman, "where will we go?" "I don't know where, but let's just go."

'I'll give you a good laugh. D'ye know what happened then? Let me tell you. But, before I do, put your drink down before you spew it all over when you start laughing. The fella that was with your brother took a fag from his pocket, lit it, and, with the still burning match, set fire to the straw mattress. My straw mattress. Up went the lot. In a matter of seconds my dear parents had one worry less. Now all they had to look for was a room. Brendan went white with temper. He raised the weapon he was carrying and, pointing it at this other fellow's head, he said, "I've a good mind to blow the fucking head off yeh, yeh bastard!" '

'And,' I asked McKevitt, 'how do you know it was Brendan?'

'I didn't know,' he replied, 'not then. But about a year later my father was reading from the paper about a boy of sixteen being sentenced on his birthday for being in possession of explosives in Liverpool. There was a picture of Brendan near the story. A bit like yourself, if I'm not mistaken. Better looking, but just as slim.'

4

'Come all young rebels and list while I sing
How love of one's land is a terrible thing
It banishes fear with the speed of a flame
And makes us all part of the Patriot game.'

WHEN I FINISHED McKevitt's story O'Hagen, the die-hard rebel, would, I knew, gladly have tried to strangle me. 'That,' he said, 'is me arse for a story. It's a slander on good men and it's a slander on yer brother.' I thought that Brendan had come out of it rather well and said so. 'Ah, don't talk bloody rubbish,' said O'Hagen. 'The same fella that told you that one is probably goin' around tellin' someone else that Brendan burned some oul fella's cart. I've never heard such nonsense.'

'Why should it be nonsense?' I asked.

'Because I'm tellin' yeh,' he insisted. 'The IRA, to my certain knowledge, never at any time interfered in the ordinary squabbles of the Northern people. By the way you're talkin' yeh'd have our crowd as bad as the bloody Orangemen.'

'I never said they did interfere, John. All I told you was what an ordinary fella told me over a drink and I can't see why he should tell me a bundle of lies.' O'Hagen looked at me with impatience. 'Maybe he knew yeh'd repeat them,' he said.

'You're a fanatic, John. The punch-up type who shouts and barracks all over the place when yeh can't get your own

37

way in an argument.' He tried hard to hold his temper as he almost shouted, 'Fanatic! I'm a fanatic?'

'Of course yeh are.' I knew I could handle him now without leaving myself in danger of a punch. 'Supposing I told you I heard something about that particular carry-on from Brendan himself?' I asked. He sneered, but his anger had quite diminished. 'Then,' he said, 'I'd say you were suffering from hallucinations. Because he could never have said it.'

'Why?' I asked. Softly he said, 'Because I was with him nearly all the time until he got himself knocked off in Liverpool at the end of '39.

'The most we ever done would be to go up as far as the border and take pot-shots at the geesers round some old RUC post. Indeed the fellas inside were so well barricaded that they hardly knew we were there half of the time. Only once did we do a job in Belfast, and that was much later. Though I'd like to add that it was a political job in case somebody tell yeh we were the Vatican's special bailiffs.' O'Hagen wore his memories like an ill-fitting hat. Trying to make up his mind about a thing. If it was still secret or could he talk about it. I could see he was bursting to speak.

'I remember we went up to Omagh in Tyrone one time and a little fella, who spoke, as Brendan said, "like himself and meself and every other Dublin jackeen were responsible for Partition", came to meet us. He told us we were to go back over the border and take up a position round a hut, close to the Monaghan Customs. Well, Brendan showered curses on the thick in Dublin who told us to go to Omagh in the first place. There we were goin' back and forward and us with a thirty-eight and fifty rounds a piece. "Brendan," says I, "would yeh ever cut out the oul bad language until we're on De Valera's side of the border, because if anyone catches us here they might do us in on the spot and forget they'd ever seen us." ' I'd heard certain stories of such a thing happening as late as 1957, but I had discounted them as so much propaganda. 'Yeh didn't really believe that,' I asked. He looked at me, wondering if I was serious and said, 'Why not? What about the way they done in Father Griffen and dumped his body in a bog?'

'Yes,' I replied, 'Brendan wrote a poem in which he mentioned that.'

'He didn't be any chance mention that Father Griffen had maybe burned some poor oulfella's cart and horse as well, while he was at it.' *Touché*, John.

'We got to this kip, anyway, and started bangin' away for a while until we realised that if there was anybody there they must be dead already. There wasn't a sign nor sound outa the place. Brendan said, "They must've resigned when they heard we were comin'." "Probably all down in some booser," I said. "Then," says Brendan, "let's go and shoot the bastards there, for, begod, it's uncommon dangerous to wage war on men fit and fortified."

'I'd have gone in a flash if it was today, and it wouldn't be to shoot anybody either. But at that time the great fashion was not only to obey an order but to be pleased at gettin' one at all. It was a most awful bloody night. Dark, wet, and cold. It was that drizzly sorta rain that people in the country are used to. Yeh know the stuff?'

'Yes,' I replied, 'we get it in the city as well.'

'Do we, begod,' said O'Hagen. 'I can't say as I ever noticed. It wasn't long, anyway, before me an' yer brother were feelin' as miserable as two monks who have just had their sack cloths taken away. We got under an oul tree an' Brendan said, "John, me love, is there no other way we can help to free Ireland than stand in the middle of a wet field and wait on some oul fogies to put the wind up them? The odds are that be the time they get here they won't know whether they themselves are Fenians or Orangemen. I'm not sure if we're not all out of our minds." "The policy is right, Brendan," I told him. "Let not one of them yokes patrol the border in peace. Terrify the bastards. Soon they'll realise that if we don't recognise the border then it doesn't exist at all." "Well," said Brendan, "if it's terrifying somebody they want, go back to Dublin and tell them they're succeedin', because, be Christ, I'm frightened out of me wits."

'"D'yeh know, Brendan," I said, "I heard two RUC men talk like you're after talkin' there now. A couple of years ago it was, when we burned the Customs huts. God, that was grand big stuff!" "I dare say it was bloody warmer, anyway," said Brendan. "I could never understand why they stopped that campaign." I told him. "Doin' too much damage, John," he replied. "In this country it's a bloody sight easier to lose a few men than half a dozen huts. Besides, it was probably thought a revolutionary destruction of property."

'"Meself and Jack Ruane lay down in a ditch," says I to Brendan, "no more than ten yards from the two RUC men and them gabbin' away to each other twenty to the dozen. There was a dirty great big moon and it had them spotlighted like a ballet dancer in the middle of a stage. Our play was to do nothin' at all until Paddy Regan who was comin' from the opposite side gave us a couple of flicks on a torch. Regan was going to throw a few petrol bombs at the hut and force them out. They must have known somethin' because they were outside already as I've said. I suppose sometimes a fella stands a better chance in the open. It was a funny thing to look at the different expressions that passed across their faces, as they stood there not knowin' from which side we were comin' but certain we were comin'.

' "One was a skinny bastard with the head of a screw an' a Thompson restin' in his arms. The other was well built with a skull head and his Thompson hung round his neck like a camera on a Yank. Except that he wasn't as casual about it, since he held tightly to the bloody thing, quick to lift it to the ready in a flash. But I'll say this for their courage, they were both as white as a well-bleached sheet. I could've picked them off as they stood but maybe they might have a couple more in the hut. Anyway, we had to wait for Regan. Did yeh ever watch two really scared men, Brendan?" He stared at me and said, "Not yet, John, but if a shot comes outa that field you're goin' to see one more. That is if the human eye can see anything as fast as I'm goin' to move outa here."

' "They'd hum a bar of a tune, Brendan, and stop. A rustle in the grass and up came the guns. The creak of a branch was enough to bring them out in sweat." "John," said Brendan, "but yeh'd do me a great service to keep that story till we're back in Phil Ryan's place drinkin' a pint." "The only thing they didn't do was run. Jazes help the poor bastards, they'd have been better off.

' "Then the skinny one went into a sort of a moan story." "What," asked Brendan, "if yeh don't mind, is a 'moan' story?" I said, "Well, it's the sort of talk yeh get up to when ye've nothin' to say. Yeh know the way kids sit around a fire at night and tell ghost stories to each other even though they're frightened out of their wits." "Now, John Hagen," said Brendan, "if yeh so much as mention the word ghost to me again this night, I'll leave yeh here to free the country be yerself. I'm not a bit afraid of the RUC but bejazes their ancestors wouldn't make me do the Walls of Limerick if they had a mind to come climbing up at me from the other side of that oul border." "I didn't mean to say they were talkin' about ghosts, Brendan. They were on about the

likes of us. As I was sayin', the skinny fella turned to skull head an' says... I won't try to imitate the accent, Brendan."
"Don't, for jazes' sake, John, or I'll die of fright."

' "Will yeh for God's sake stop interruptin'," I said. " 'Eh, Sandy. Did yeh hear tell of what happened to Billy Williams down Newry way last week?' 'I didn't, then,' said the skull head, 'what did happen to him?' 'Well,' said the skinny one, 'them IRA fellas marched in and made poor Billy lie down on the ground an' swear to uphold the Republic. An' then for good measure they made him sing "Kevin Barry". Isn't that damnable?' 'Oh,' said the other fella, 'damnable altogether.' 'An' his father a grandmaster of the Orange Lodge.' 'But tell me,' said the skull, 'how come that a loyal son of the Orange Lodge's grandmaster should know the words of "Kevin Barry"?' " "Oh merciful God!" said Brendan. "What's wrong?" I asked. "John," he replied, "I can't remember the words of 'God Save the Queen'." "Will yeh stop trickin' about," says I, "for Christ sake, and let me finish the story." "I will not for yer goin' to tell me somethin' dreadful. God, isn't it terrible to belong to an army that has no one else to entertain the troops at the front but yerself?"

' "At that moment, Brendan, I saw the flash of Regan's torch comin' three times from the other side of the field. I turned to Ruane and said, 'Let the bastards have it. Now!' I never saw anything like it, Brendan. The skinny fella went down like an empty sack, and there was nothin' but a look of astonishment in his kisser. Neither of them uttered so much as a squeal. Never knew what hit them."

' "Well," said Brendan, "are yeh quite happy now? What in the namea God d'ye want to go tellin' me things like that for? Begod but I'm bad enough without you puttin' the heart across me. Why couldn't yis have just taken the poor whores without killin' them?" "And them armed with

Thompsons? Brendan," I said, "if you've a mind to drink a few pints in Dublin, get them thoughts out of yer head." '

There was neither satisfaction nor sorrow in O'Hagen's storytelling. It was as though he had just read aloud the runners and riders for the three o'clock. I don't think regret contributed anything at all to his emotional make-up. Yet I had to ask him, 'Did yeh have to kill them, John?' Without hesitating he answered, 'We had thirty-eights. They had Thompsons. No match. Let me explain. Remember I said Brendan and I did only one job inside the North of Ireland? Well, that was some years after what I've been tellin' yeh. Brendan had already done his time in England, in fact, and this was shortly before Dev's crowd sent him to the Curragh. A raid was carried out on a payroll in the North and all yer brother and I had to do was take certain things from there to Dublin.'

The money, I thought, but I knew had O'Hagen wanted to tell me he would have done so.

'I won't tell yeh what the job was but if yeh ever read a book by F. L. Greene called *Odd Man Out* yeh'll know the sort of thing it was. The story was very similar to this.

'Now, I don't know anything about the actual raid but what I've been told because I wasn't there when the payroll was commandeered. But a kid of sixteen involved in it got himself shot to pieces because he wouldn't shoot a policeman who was kneeling with his back to him. The rozzer was attendin' to some other fella that had been hit and as the chissler ran for the getaway car the peeler nips smartly around, he ups with a Thompson, and cut the young fella to ribbons.'

'What was his name?' I asked.

O'Hagen shook his head and said, 'I won't tell yeh that, Dominic, because there are people belongin' to him still alive and it might be painful to them.

43

'When we arrived at the spot where we were to pick up the other things we found that we had to transfer this young fella to our car and get him some medical treatment. So the lad was shoved into the back seat between Brendan and meself, and we drove off.

'On the way I'll never forget that brother of yours. The kid was absolutely writhing in agony and Brendan said, sensibly enough, that the best thing to do would be to stop somewhere and get a bottle of brandy. Even the boy himself said he'd like a drink. Dominic,' said O'Hagen, 'God forgive me for laughin' but . . D'ye know that bit in *The Hostage* where Brendan says that when a fella has a fainne in his coat to denote he can speak Irish——'

'Yes,' I interrupted, 'he says that he must be an officer in the IRA, and if he has a pledge-pin to say he doesn't drink, he must be a higher officer.'

'Well,' O'Hagen went on, 'if that be the case, then the bastard who was drivin' this car must have been at least the Chief of Staff, for he'd a fainne, a pledge-pin, and more badges to say he didn't do this or wouldn't do that than I've ever seen.'

'Had he got one for keepin' away from women?' I asked.

'The only whore that'd be stupid enough to have anything to do with this eejit,' said O'Hagen, 'would be a bloody virgin.'

'Anyway, this anti-gargle fanatic turns to the kid when he says he'd fancy a drink and lets loose a torrent of abuse. "Drink!" he roared, like a Redemptorist preaching fire and brimstone on the HP. "Drink! Man alive, it's thinkin' of yer God yeh should be. Besides, it'd all come out you're so full of holes!" '

O'Hagen choked back a laughter ball that had got stuck in his throat and kept repeating through his coughs 'Drink! Yer God yeh should be thinking of an' you so full of holes!'

Suddenly it struck me in a flash that Brendan had mentioned the chap's name one time 'Dusty!' I said, 'Dusty Flynn!' O'Hagen stopped laughing and his face went quite pale. 'I'll say nothin'!' he whispered. 'Nothin'!' Then almost to himself he murmured, 'Whatever his name was he's at peace now. May the Lord be good to him.'

I knew almost as much about that raid as O'Hagen did himself. The job was legendary. Why should he be so upset at my mentioning his name? I remember buying lilies to send to the funeral – green lilies grown only in the minds of Easter Republicans. *Republican War News* carried stories of 'Innocent Boy Brutally Murdered by Imperialist Lackeys'. And yet something strange there was about that year 1942. Paddy McGrath and Tommy Harte were executed, in the South of Ireland other men got killed, the lad O'Hagen spoke of went down, but only one man is remembered in song around that time, Tom Williams hanged in Belfast and the boy for whom Brendan made the British soldier Leslie pay for with his life in *The Hostage*. When Brendan was drunk he would sing of the year '42:

'That sad October morn when Ireland's cross was
    proudly borne,
By a lad who sleeps in a Belfast Prison grave.'

In Brendan's and O'Hagen's 1942 they were stricken by a disease for which they had no name then. Nowadays we know that they were teenagers.

That was the year I celebrated my fourteenth birthday by being promoted an O/C in 'Na Fianna Eireann' – because anybody better suited for the job was already behind bars. 'Finish the story yeh started, John,' I asked O'Hagen. He thought for a moment and said, 'I finished it.' 'Then,' said I, 'yeh mean it ended with yourself and Brendan standin' in the middle of the field?'

'Oh aye. Omagh? Well, there's nothin' much to tell, really.' It seemed that O'Hagen was either trying to forget something or remember, a bit of both maybe. 'It rained more heavily,' he carried on, 'and soon there seemed nothin' in the world but sheets of water. And we tried to smoke. Silly thing to do. Cigarettes wet and damp. And a mist behind the rain. Like wipin' the windscreen of a car on a bad night and lookin' out at the shadows. That was the trouble I suppose. The shadows were in our minds. It was so dense, the atmosphere, that the shadows could never have existed but in our minds.'

I looked at O'Hagen. He wasn't aware of my presence at all. I'm not surprised, because I've seen a lot of men from his time and it doesn't matter for what they've killed or known others to be killed, they're all a bit like O'Hagen. He was talking on and on, getting mechanically to the end of the story. I couldn't have stopped him even had I wanted. 'Everything was closing in around us. Not just the weather, but people in it. Our feet were stuck to the ground and the edge of my trenchcoat lapel was brushing against my neck. Funny how a little thing like that can make yeh aware of yourself – aware, I mean, that you're alive and doin' somethin' dangerous, aware that yeh may not be much longer alive. Suddenly the mist cleared a bit and the rain was light. They say yeh don't get mist with rain so I suppose it must have been a shortage of light. I could see a few feet in front of me and my forehead was wetter than it had been, sweat. I was covered in bloody sweat.

'We were actually standin' in the same position as those RUC men before they got the hammer. The strange thing is that neither of us tried to talk. Then I saw something move at the bottom of the field where the light was good. I fired into a waving hedge once, twice, three times. I fired four shots into that hedge that waved and it stopped movin'.' I remembered Brendan when he was drunk shortly before he died and he'd tell you the same story over and over, re-enacting the shooting for which he was sentenced to fourteen years in '42, 'I shot them! I shot them! I shot the bastards!' He had fired five rounds from a thirty-eight and missed with all five.

O'Hagen said, 'We waited. I don't know how long we waited. But nothin' came from behind the hedge. I advanced towards it slowly and I signalled Brendan to follow. We got to the hedge and heard a groan or somethin'. I shoved the thirty-eight through a gap in the hedge and went after it. Yeh know, I've an idea I closed me eyes. On the other side of the hedge was a nearly dead cow. "Ah," said Brendan, "the poor oul thing." I whispered to him to put a round through the animal's head, but he stared at the revolver as though it was too dreadful. He turned his back and I fired. My God, the report was like a thunderclap! The poor oul beast shit for the last time and as true as jazes, Dominic, the ground was scarlet.'

5

'And in Kilkenny it is reported on marble stones there
   as black as ink
That with gold and silver I would support her
Ach I'll sing no more till I've had a drink
But I've been drinking I'm seldom sober
   a constant rover from town to town
Now I'm sick and me days are over
Come mair a'stoir and I'll lay me down.'

WITH A GRANNY AND TWO AUNTS doing time for the cause I was a popular figure in the young Republican circles of south-west Dublin where my brother was at that time virtually unknown. Brendan's arrest in 1939 while on the way to distribute hard-got Republican gelignite among the shipbuilders of Cammell Laird's, Liverpool, made me even more popular. When he delivered a highly romantic speech in which he defended the ideal of an Irish Workers' and Small Farmers' Republic and received three years' borstal training from an attentive judge, who regretted that because of his age he couldn't make it a bit longer, there was no more popular rebelager than I from Kimmage to Kilmashogue.

They released him in 1942 and just when it seemed that he might become more famous for his deeds than I, he was sentenced to fourteen years by what we used to call Colonel

Joyce's Military Tribunal. If he made a speech on this occasion only the Colonel and his fellow officers heard it, for Mr De Valera, with a near monopoly on his own sort of Republicanism, had no intention of giving publicity to the patriotic sort.

When the war ended, De Valera's people had little excuse for retaining the Emergency Powers with which they had vested themselves for the fight against Britain and Germany and under which Act they interned masses of folk who had entertained notions of a free country. The prisoners were released and Brendan was among them.

I was nearing the end of my reign as the undisputed authority on Brendan when he was arrested for violation of a deportation order and sentenced to six months. He had gone to England to aid the escape of a republican from Parkhurst Prison in 1948. Brendan must have been one of the most captured soldiers in the history of Irish revolt.

In the few months Brendan had been with the world from his release in early '46 his name had become a legend in the history of Dublin house-painting. He made a deep and lasting impression on workers, bosses, and foremen and he had written an anthem for the trade:

'Hand me down me paper knife, and me stirring stick,
Hand me down me overalls we've a big job in the nick,
The boss is a quare one fall di do yeh gow a that
A quare and a rare one I'll tell you.
In the cold hard wintertime they have us on a cross
Stuck up like Christ between two thieves, the foreman
    and the boss
Who is it that we're workin' for? It isn't he called
    "sir",
He has a whore in Monto Town and ye chokin' yer balls
    for her.

The autumn leaves are falling, the night s are getting dim
There's not a stroke to be done till March so hand your
brushes in.'

Its first recital was given by my brother at a gathering of
painters in Government Buildings, Dublin, who had been
intimidated by Brendan down from their various posts of
labour. And when an astonished foreman landed in the
middle of this apprehensive audience and sacked Brendan
on the spot, my brother grovelled at the man's feet, kissed
the hem of his raincoat, and pleaded, 'Don't sack me, sir,
I've a publican and five little barmen dependent upon me.'

He was fond of quoting Dylan Thomas' 'A job is a death
without dignity'. And if it works the other way round I
dare say that there are at least one thousand members of
the decorating trade ready to swear that Brendan Behan
was the most dignified painter in Dublin.

'Is Brendan Behan your brother?' the foreman asked. I
hesitated for a moment, not knowing if I should admit to
the relationship. 'Well?' he demanded. Sadly I nodded my
head in the affirmative and waited to be told that my cards
and money were ready in the office, 'I've arranged with Miss
Murphy that you can collect your pay, back pay, and
holiday pay, and since you'll be away some time I think
you should maybe take your cards as well. When he's better
– as please God he will – look in and I might have something
for you. Now there's a train to Cork at six o'clock and if
you hurry you should manage to catch it.'

'What's wrong?' I said. 'Why should I want to go to
Cork?'

'Oh,' he answered sympathetically, 'I thought you knew
about your brother?'

'What about him?' I asked. He didn't know how to tell
me, then, with an air of 'tragedy brings even the high and

the lowly together' he said, 'Brendan has been seriously injured in a car accident and is anxious to see you.' He was anxious to see me, all right. As I emerged sorrowfully from the office, clutching my cards and money, he pounced. 'It worked! I knew it would. Give us at least half. I'm entitled to it because it was me that thought the scheme up.' It seemed I was going to die with dignity as well.

Tom Fogarty stopped my father and invited him to sup with him in Sinnots of South King Street. He was an old friend of Da's and for that reason my father gave ear to his worries as a foreman painter. 'Stephen,' he said, 'I'm in charge of the painting on a new hospital building and I'm positively distracted. In the name of God where are the great painters of our day?'

'Dead from starvation, cholic, and overwork, Tom,' answered my father. 'Oh, but look here, Stephen, I'm not the sort of chargehand would want a man to turn his arse into an umbrella for me, but I have with me now two of the greatest bastards! The greatest bastards I've ever come across. One wants the men to strike for an incentive bonus so that the other one can bring them down to the pub to drink it. And now they told me this mornin' they want a five-day week, the only difference being that they want Monday off and double time for Saturday and Sunday. I've a little office on the bottom floor of the hospital and it was the mercy of God somebody heard me shouting or I might be there yet. They had me locked in. Would yeh credit it? Oh, the greatest bastards. I've tried sackin' them but they're always sent back as being the first men on the Union books, and if I don't take them I get no one. Bad enough with the first fella, Brendan, all he wanted to do was drink, but when the other fella arrived and stopped the work for a principle I thought I'd go mad.' Poor Tom, may the Lord be good to him, was so distracted that he forgot to whom he was talking, but, as my father said years later when somebody asked him about Brendan and me, 'Well, I married their mother, and now my only hope is that the Lamb of God should turn into the Ram of God and fuck the two of them!'

We had only worked together in about five decorating shops when the other two hundred or so employers heard about the notorious Brendan Behan and his brother. From then on I exercised my right under the constitution to use the Irish form of my name, 'O'Beacain', on my insurance cards. A foreman would say, 'German, huh?' as he shoved the cards into his pocket, and though I lost my name and identity I kept my job.

Brendan, however, couldn't have hidden himself had he translated his name into Sanskrit, and the only work I remember him doing then was the front of Tom Nisbett's Grafton Galleries. God help yeh, Tom, but yeh were a brave man.

The Grafton Galleries and John McDaid's pub are a married pair in a block of buildings in Harry Street. It is Tom Nisbett's Grafton Street local. Tom had a sculptor friend called Des McNamara who knew Brendan since childhood, and Ena Murphy knew Tom because she worked as his receptionist, and her friend was Mr Richard Wyman, who rented a flat at 13a FitzWilliam Place, and people came to stay there when they had no money and, of course, they drank in McDaid's because it was Tom's local. Time was when you could go into that decent public house and talk about the most ordinary things and not a sinner soul raked the ashes of your conversation for the hidden symbolism. And then somebody brought along a copy of James Joyce's banned in Ireland, *Ulysses*. Up to then the literati had met in the Palace Bar in Fleet Street, because the most they could hope for was a few guineas' worth of space in the *Irish*

Times edited by Bob Smiley, who also drank at the Palace. Then they got wind of the word that a strange character called Brendan Behan, known on occasions to be of brilliant conversational disposition, held forth a little way up the road, each morning, evening, and afternoon as had a night to them.

It was an unusual sight, a man who between Kafka and Guinness would dash outside, brush in hand, to check a paint run on Tom's gallery and return to pick up the drink and the story where he had left it. Only a brave man would dare to meddle with either in his absence. Other people came too. 'That great cultural phenomena,' Brendan called them, 'the progeny of the gentry and the bourgeoisie, their only function to give sustenance to the artist on the money robbed by their ancestors.' Included among this class was Mr Osbert Podmore.

I was working out in a Dublin suburb when Brendan rang and asked me if I knew it was Friday. 'I'll meet yeh in McDaid's pub at half-six. Come down Grafton Street from the Green and yeh'll find it's the second turn on the left.' It seemed that 'Messrs Burton, Tailors of Taste' would get nothing from my pay packet this week, either.

'This is Dominic, my brother,' he announced to the company, and they nodded their heads, those who cared. One little man, Ned Sheehy, an art critic in high gumboots, took an interest in me and told people who came in after me, 'This is Dominic, Brendan's brother.' Because the public had not as yet settled down, Brendan called on me to sing, and spoke as I sang about there bein' 'nothin' like a nice young voice'. Then I gave him the money for which he had been waiting and he lost all further interest in me.

I was on the point of leaving, but Sheehy prevailed upon me to remain and received from Brendan an angry glare. Brendan the extrovert seemed quite inhibited in the presence of any member of his family. Soon I slipped happily into conversation with Sheehy, who told me I had a good mind. Since nobody as literate as a man who had on occasions written for Mr Smiley's paper had ever said that to me before I began to feel entitled to drink a pint here. I ignored Brendan's glassy stares, and as my brother drank more his inhibitions became less and soon he didn't give a damn who was in the company. 'What d'ye think of Joyce?' asked a thin ascetic-looking student. 'They shouldn't have hanged him,' replied Brendan, and turned to greet Ena Murphy, who sat with a pint of stout between Sheehy and I.

'Ah, Ena, my mee na,' said Brendan, 'all the way from merry Kerry with the accent gone and in its place a voice that would be accepted by Lady Bracknell herself.' Ena was aged about forty, tall, with a long face set off by two radiant eyes shining in anticipation of joys to come. 'You've forgotten where yeh come from, Ena,' said Brendan, 'the Left Bank and Piccadilly have wiped away the land of your fathers and mothers, aye and grandmothers. Yeh'd never dream of splittin' an ould infinitive with a peasant these days or – as they would maybe have said in your granny's days – those days. Down in dat part of Ireland where dey speak the best English known to English-speakin' men – hello der, Dan!' Ena sat enraptured. I sat amazed that she was drinking a pint of Guinness and holding it like it was a medium-dry sherry in the hand of a débutante. Brendan hoisted the collar of his coat over his head until the small of the back of the jacket stood firmly on the centre of his black hair and he was for all the world like an old Irish shawled woman of the roads. A young man entered, wearing a deerstalker and carrying a stick. 'Is yer poor leg better, Podmore, a stoir mo croidhe tiddly dee with a bedad and a begororrah – I'll leave besodom out to keep the party clean.'

'There's nothing wrong with my leg, Brendan,' replied

Podmore in a soft English accent. 'And for what might yeh be after carryin' a stick through the big town of Dublin, me trasure bright. Ah, sure isn't it meself knows that it's hankerin' after bein' Irish yeh are. For I'd have yeh know, me fine friend in ascendant adversary, no real Irishman wields a stick unless somethin' is the matter with his bottom limbs.' The young man smiled, rather foolishly I thought, and Ena interrupted. 'Now, Brendan, leave poor Osbert alone, he doesn't know that you're only joking.'

'Ah sure, indeed he does, don't yeh? Poor Podmore, how are yeh! and how many millions is yer daddy down to today, poor Podmore? Though I will admit yeh show shockin' good taste in wantin' to be Irish. But make sure, Podmore, yeh know Ireland, "that lovely land", as Joyce called her, "that always sent her writers and artistes to banishment and in a spirit of Irish fun betrayed her leaders one by one. It was Irish humour wet and dry flung quicklime into Parnell's eye, O Ireland, my first and only love, where Christ and Caesar are hand in glove." '

'Excuse me, Mr Ehh . . .' said Mr McDaid, who never called anybody by name, 'but that'll be four-an'-six.'

'An' no better man than me to pay it, Mr Mac,' said Brendan. 'Tell me,' he asked of an earnest young man who listened with increasing frown, 'do I owe yeh anythin'?' The young man flushed and said, 'I was just listenin' to the outrageous remarks yeh were makin' about the country.'

'Yeh don't agree with them, like?' asked Brendan.

'I certainly do not,' said the young man.

'Then,' said Brendan, 'fuck off and listen to other conversations more in tune with your stupid nature.' He was getting drunk, drunk and angry and stammering; he always stammered when he was angry and he became angry when he realised he had given offence. 'Sing us a song, Brendan,' said Ena. 'And,' replied Brendan, 'no better man, and you,' he turned to me, 'I could sing you into a cocked bastardin' hat!' He had a very good voice when sober but now he started shouting and he knew it wasn't too good. He got back to his pet subject – Ireland.

'Ireland,' said Brendan, 'is a village in Trieste with James Joyce; Devon with Sean O'Casey; Paris with Sam Beckett and all tied together, from O'Neill in America to Wilde in Reading Jail to an elderly degenerate proselytising umbilical lasoo known as the Archbishop of Dublin. Ireland is a figment of the Anglo-Saxon imagination, her vices extolled as virtues and her glorious memory perpetuated by Boss Croker and Tammany Hall. Ireland is a lie, a state or place non-existent since St Patrick was a Highlander and the First of the Clan Yeats sailed into Killala Bay armed with cudgels and speaking Danish with a lisp. Why ask me about Ireland when we could just as easily discuss the chances of the favourite in the Derby? Because I want you rebel drunkards to know what Ireland means! I'll tell you a story which would have been a lie had it not gained the blessing of the folk-poets. Folk-tales,' said Brendan, 'always begin in the middle, and this one is no exception. I'll have to tell it in me best accent.

'And every morning we were up before dawn had time to stretch its limbs and we would go down to the sea to take in the lobster pots. Sometimes there were three or two or one in each. Sometimes the pots were empty and we knew the cloth would have to be cut to our measure for the next little while. "Making a manage", the women called it, and we tried not to think of the pig we might have to sell and winter not with us for another month yet. We knew it was His Holy Will and if we didn't nobody ever let on.

'It was God's Holy Will when a boat turned over in the rough sea and hurled the men on to the waters to go down or be saved as God's Holy Will might decree. And it was

God's Holy Will that men and women boys and girls were lost to America. I don't think I can remember a time when it wasn't the Will of God and I suppose it must have been the Will of somebody else before He came into the lives of us.

'We knew everything about the lobster but his taste, for we couldn't afford to eat him. Indeed we would never have been interested in reaping such a harvest had it not been that someone somewhere else liked the eating of him and so made a living in the catching. But that wasn't in my time or my father's or his.

'The lobster fields were three or four miles off the coast and the sea there was a different colour – reddish black in the blue and green adeep. But on some mornings the waters tossed all over the boat so that we daren't brave their fierce anger and we returned to the mainland wet and with sorrow little else but our lives for our pains. This would be the time when the women would say, "Ah, God is good," and sure enough a letter would arrive that day from the States with a little money from one who had travelled a greater distance in one voyage than we had sailed in five lifetimes. We saw American dollars long before we knew the colour of our own country's money and that's a fact.

'Now all our folk are as black-haired as the hob of hell. Our fathers were black and their fathers before them. Ship-wrecked Spaniards invaded our blood, or so they say. True or false, it doesn't make any matter to the way we live, we depended on the Will of God for all things good or bad until he came to live among us.

'We took him from the sea, a dead man, and the priest rolled him over on to his back, pushing him and prodding him until he began to live again. And he worked his limbs up and down and sideways and after a while we were to move him to a house where the priest would carry on with his treatment until the face of the red-haired man lost its blue look and he opened his eyes.

'For as many days as it takes to set the pots and bring them in again he lay in the corner of the house and we knew he was getting the better of his illness by the way his eyes began to follow the every movement of every person who passed his way. His now pale face took an interest in all that went on, but his lips never formed one single word so that we didn't know if he had always been dumb or if maybe the sea was to blame. And if he was interested in us it was as nothing compared to our sight of a red-haired man.

'He was the talk of the whole place and a ballad was made about his flaming head and it was sung in the evenings when the work was done. But our ballad-maker, who is also a cripple, added another stave about red hair being the sign of the devil's hand on God's work. For a long time that stave was left out by the folk because we knew that the little cripple was a bitter one who always blamed his own trouble on the fine-looking men and women about him. Then the stranger was well enough to walk, and walk he did, head erect. He was a tower of a man and the eyes of the whole place turned in his wake whenever he passed by. The young unmarried women gave secret glances up from their work and the old married females sighed for another chance.

'It must have been the young men who started to sing the cripple's verse to the ballad first, and I suppose it was with good reason in a place where wives are hard to come by when the youth are saving all the time for the day when they can leave us behind forever except for the makings of a letter. But soon every man was singing about the red-haired man being the work of the devil and it didn't stop at that.

'He went out with us to the sea and proved himself as

fine a boatsman ever I'm likely to see in my lifetime, thank God. Whatever we did he did with less effort and, because he didn't speak, he worked all the harder, and he wasn't so feared of the rough sea as other men, but sat in the boat, his face to the wind and a sort of a smile playing around his silent lips.

'Then it was no longer the Will of God for everything. Only what was good was God's Will. What was bad was the will of the devil and the devil began to take on the appearance of a tall handsome man with red hair. Nets had been empty and pots had been without lobsters before, but nobody remembered that now. Only it had happened since we took the stranger from the sea among us.

'At first this was only said behind his back and behind the back of the priest, then the men seemed not to care but believing in the truth of what they had to say, said it. When a man can't speak what matter if something unpleasant is said about him to his face?

'Of course, the priest spoke to us sternly about the evil of calumniation and for a while the ballad was left unsung and the harsh words unspoken. Until one morning four of the men and the red-haired one left to bring in the pots. We never knew what happened out there, for the stranger who swam back to the coast spoke nothing and the puffed up white-faced corpses we took from the sea ten days after spoke less. But it was agreed that the work of the devil had been done and even the priest gave fearful looks now towards the red-haired man, or so it seemed.

'The stranger stayed away from the burial and it was clear to the whole place that this was the act of one who could not face the folk they had left behind. It was not godly that a man should stay far from those who had died when he was saved and the people fell to thinking that maybe the little cripple had been more right than many had allowed.

Nor had the cripple been idle. All this time he had been making ballads most powerful about the man from the sea and they hinting and pointing at the evilness in blood-red hair. The head was the head of a murderer and all the blackness had gone to his devil's heart. It was to be that we would never have another minute of God's peace until we drove this man from the place as we would drive a pig to the fair. He would be the ruination of our wives, and no man's daughter or woman could ever again call safety her own. What else could we do but hunt him off as we would a fox from the hills? Could we leave him and no man in the place but a cripple? For to sea we couldn't take him and he after murdering four strong men with his bare hands and while out on the waters. But if we did drive him away over the hills we didn't know but maybe he would return the way he went, and at night.

'Only the cripple could tell us what to do and he asked us to pause a while and think if there was one among us of whom none was afraid. Then he told us that he was that one man and that the reason none had any need to fear him was because he was like no other person in that place. He was only a half-man. The cripple told us that the commandments of the Church told us how wrong it was to kill, but there was no rule laid down about doing to the red-haired man what God in His most merciful wisdom had done to the cripple. The stranger must be left without his strength and shorn of his red hair, it would be the Will of God to maim the man and none could doubt the Will of the Almighty.

'They had smoked little more than two pipes of tobacco when they saw the flaming red hair floating as it were on top of the green ferns. Silently they crossed themselves and then, falling on the big man with their cudgels, they beat him this way and that so that the only sound to come from the stranger was the cracking of his ribs and the breaking of his arms and legs. Then they half dragged, half carried him to the house where only a little while before he had recovered from a near drowning. The little ballad-maker was there to gloat, but when he saw the condition of the red-haired man he turned on the assailants with scarifying tongue and upbraided them no end. What sort of men were they, he wanted to know, that couldn't break the back of one lone creature. His arms and legs would mend, as would his ribs, and instead of leaving him an object of pity they had put him in a position from which he would gain the sympathy of the whole place. It was for them now to break his back and all that required was one hefty blow from a stick. But no man was there who wanted to do more than had already been done, for the light was shining on the red-haired man now and beyond the darkness of night it wasn't good to look upon such handiwork. Some among them were even given to the thought that the cripple had unspoken fears for the day when the red-haired man would walk stiffly erect again.'

'Mr Eh,' said Mr McDaid, 'yer wanted on the telephone.'

Brendan bowed low to the company and made his way to the telephone. He said, for all to hear, 'I'm pleased, I'm bloody delighted, your message could not have come at a better time, for there is an old folk-collector ready in the corner with ninety-nine verses of a border ballad and a sculptor who will outdo Henry Moore if he gets his hands into some clay. Not to talk of drunken Ena looking long and lovingly at Edward Sheehy's rubber seaboots. Buy them now! The latest thing in Catholic contra-contraception. Guaranteed twelve children a week. Yes, I thought you might like that, yeh filthy gett. Particularly if they're all male. Goodbye for ever, or for ever goodbye.'

'What happened?' asked Ena. 'Bertie Wilson wants us to

bring a few bottles back to his place,' he replied, 'and,' turning to me he said, 'you could come too, if yeh buy my dozen of Guinness as well as yer own.' Ena pulled at his jacket. 'I meant what happened to the red-haired man.'

'Begod,' said Brendan, 'a woman for yer life. I might have known the idea of a big, strappin', unusually silent, ginger-headed brute would interest yeh more than a telephone call. They say women like silent men. Thank God I've never met a silent woman, I'd hate that. On the other hand Gainor says he slept with a mute.' 'The red-haired man,' said Ena. 'Well now, my love, how in Christ's name would I know, for I was never down that far in Ireland in me life. Though I will say one thing, he's a lucky man that never opened his mouth or they'd have fucking killed him alto-gether. Hatred of the unusual comes easily to a people with suffering on their backs and tradition at their finger-tips.'

Some nodding young men in duffel-coats sat to ponder the message in Brendan's words as my brother, passing them at the bar, said to Ena, 'On the other hand again. 'Tis said Madame Lafarge loved one-legged men. So long as the amputation affected only the left or the right one and never the leg in the middle.'

Wedding Day—Mr and Mrs Dominic Behan. Brendan Behan
was Best Man. Front row: J. Quinn, Mrs N. Dahlstrom,
Dominic and Josephine Behan, Mrs R. Furlong, Miss M.
Quinn; back row: J. K. Quinn, Rory Furlong, Mrs B. Quinn,
Brendan and Beatrice Quinn.

Family and friends of Stephen Behan, taken when Stephen
was the subject in BBC Television's 'This Is Your Life.'

Brendan Behan, with Beatrice his wife and
Desmond McNamara.

Brendan and Beatrice Behan.

Brendan in the drink!

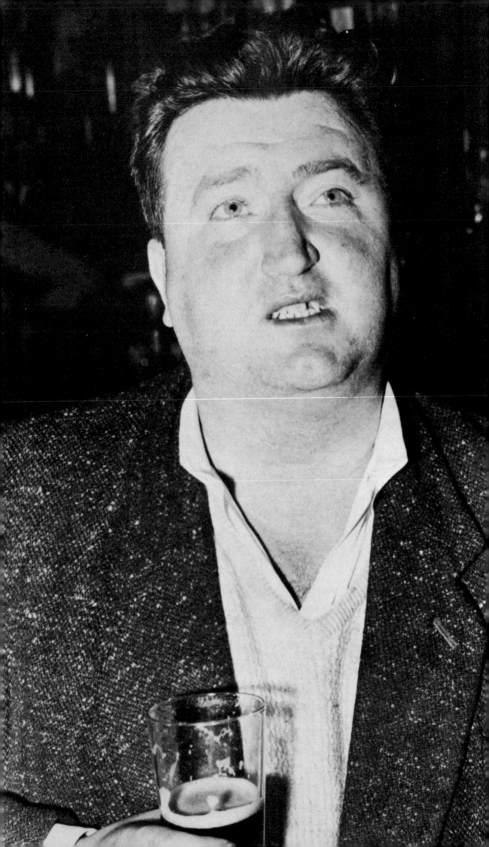

6

'Feathered beds are soft
Painted rooms are bonnie
I would leave them all
To go with my love Johnny.'

AT THE *Sign of the Zodiac* Burgundy retailed at five shillings per flagon and it was only when McDadian party-goers were going to their respective functions that they patronised this public house opposite McDaid's. 'I'll carry the Guinness,' said Brendan, handing one of the dozens to Ena and the other to Osbert Podmore, 'while you slip across the road and get about four bottles of "Goudle".' ' "Goudle",' explained Ena, 'is our name for Burgundy.'

'But, Brendan,' I said, and dropping my voice to a whisper, 'I've no money.' He stood in the middle of the road and shouted, 'No money! And yeh were only paid today! Don't yeh get nearly nine pounds a week, man?' He pretended to beg from passers by on my behalf and slowly swinging into a complete act said to Ena, 'Did yeh ever see the beggar women on O'Connell Bridge? "God bless yeh, sir. Thank yeh, sir. May the blessin's of God follow yeh, sir," and when she gets nothin' for her trouble she shouts after the mean man, "An' never catch up with yeh! Yeh miserable oul bastard!" '

Turning in mid-sentence to tell me, 'Sure yeh couldn't have spent nine nicker tonight?'

'Well, I have me mother's money,' I replied. 'And what's

wrong with me mother's money? If they say one bad word about me mother, or anything belongin' to her, I'll be in there like a shot. Yer as bad as Paddy Fanning who used to say, "Mother, I love yeh! An' if anythin' ever happened to yeh I'd throw meself off Blackwire Bridge!" Bejazes he hadn't the psychosis all that bad, for there's been nothin' but a green lawn on the other side of Blackwire Bridge since Noah drove a tug for Guinness' Brewery up the Liffey with fourteen coopers of brown stout. And yeh'd hardly believe it, but if he hadn't saved that, during the forty-day drought, we'd go thirsty this minute.'

Podmore said, 'It's alright, Dominic, I'll pay for it.'

'There yeh are,' Brendan laughed, 'he's not mindin' about spendin' his mother's money, been spendin' it for years, haven't yeh, Podmore?' Podmore slipped his hand into his inside pocket and turned his back as he examined his wallet, 'There he is,' said Brendan, 'selectin' the wheat from the chaff. Begod, Ena, could yeh ever imagine me with a wallet?'

'I could not, dear,' replied Ena, 'and I could picture yeh less with anything to put into it.'

'They used to make them in the Curragh when I was interned there. And Celtic Crosses to Republicans murdered by De Valera, from matchsticks. Then they had more matches than contemporary heroes and they started lookin' through history. When they let us out a fella had one nearly finished in honour of Lugh of the long arm. That was one reason I was sorry over bein' released because I was dyin' to see his face when I'd tell him that he had stuck fifty thousand Christian matches together in honour of a pagan.' Podmore handed me a pound note and I went across to the *Zodiac*.

When I came out carrying four bottles of Burgundy, Harry Street was deserted, and for an instant I thought that my brother had decided a pound would be a cheap price at which to get rid of me. Then from the direction of Grafton Street I heard his voice singing loudly, lusty, lewd songs. I caught up with the party as they reached the corner of College Green, where Brendan admonished an astonished elderly gentleman with the warning, 'I've told yeh once, an' I'll tell you no more, keep away from my granny.'

On O'Connell Bridge he knelt to a portly priest and begged post absolution for future transgressions, and when that gentleman looked contemptuously at him he treated the priest to a short history of the clergy in Irish politics. 'In the penal days,' he said when the priest had passed, 'the people used to hide their pastor in a chimney. They'd have to build one around that fellow.'

'There yeh are,' said a man at the cab rank outside the Gresham Hotel. 'Hello, whacker!' replied Brendan, and turning to Ena he asked and answered, 'D'ye see that fella? Well, he's one of the Virtues from Corporation Buildings and his brother was one time in the IRA. Oh a stupid eejit! A friend of mine gave him a packet of Beecham's powders with which to poison the reservoir supplyin' Camden Town in London and he let him out of his sight first and then spilled the stuff all over the road. Says he to a friend, "Sure my sister Molly lives down in that place." But, as I was sayin', one of our intelligence men – God bless the mark – found out he was a police tout – probably heard he'd informed the castle we were goin' to hold a public meeting in O'Connel Street. Anyway, we rolled over to where he lived, in the middle of the night, and painted all around the place, "Beware of Virtue the Spy". When the burglar class got to see it they thought poor Virtue was after bein' givin' information about *them*. Jazes, they knocked hell out of the poor bastard.'

At the junction of Parnell Street and Gardiner Street with

an expansive wave he said, 'Now yer in my country. Look at the death of the Empire in the desecration of their property. All those slums were once the town houses of the gentry. The Corporation is going to restore them, though, and a clever touch! Real people in hundreds of flats behind a Georgian façade. If anybody asks how the Empire died tell them the Irish turned it into a tenement.' An old woman stumbled at the corner of Mountjoy Square and as Brendan helped her to her feet she said gratefully, 'Ah, Brendan Behan, isn't it good to know that there's still one gentleman alive in Dublin, even if it's only a dirty bloody bousey like yerself.' Brendan laughed his way across Mountjoy Square to Bertie Wilson's.

At the bottom of the basement steps stood a tall man smiling. He held a cigarette between index and middle finger of his right hand with his thumb inclined towards the palm. His pale grey suit was tailor-patched at the knees and the carnation in his jacket looked at home. 'My dears,' he trilled, 'Mafeking is relieved to see you. Mr McDaid charged you on each bottle, no doubt?' Brendan said, 'Three shillin's on every sacred dozen.'

'How nice,' sang Bertie, 'only last week I took back a brigade of empties to that horrid Murphy's and the dreadful man merely said, "Thank you very much, sir, it's not often people bring them back on their own." I'm bloody certain it's not. Three jangling miles to the accompaniment of ragged children asking if I was giving balloons for rags.'

Bertie held his cheek to Ena and, when she had kissed it, he asked, 'And who, my dear, is this sweet boy?'

Brendan said, 'He has the extremely good fortune to be my brother, though what terrible sin I committed on me parents I can't think. He's young, I'll grant yeh, and through no great effort on his part. But sweet? Well, I'd never mistake him for a chocolate drop. Now would yeh ever let us in before the workin' class gets to know the type of bloody blackguards I'm consortin' with since I decided that literature was a better trade than workin'?' I extended my hand and as Bertie shook it I said, 'My name is Dominic.' Brendan exploded into mock laughter and said, 'Oh, I forgot to tell yeh, he's also a conversationalist. Tell me,' he asked, while I blushed freely, 'did yeh say that yerself? D'ye mind if I make a note of your sayings?'

'Now, Brendan,' said Bertie, as we entered his flat, 'no naughtiness tonight, dear.' And turning to me he said, 'You have no idea, Dominic, how that brother of yours behaves. Only last week a dear friend of mine was sharing my boudoir with the wife of another dear friend, while at the same time Brendan was having a long and involved intellectual discussion with the lady's husband out here,' and he indicated the room in which we were sitting. 'On the pretext of going to the Lu, he crept in to where the happy couple were and loosened the screws of the bed and after a while the unfortunate pair fell helplessly to the floor. Very naughty of you, Brendan, David might not have been aware of their liaison.'

Two women sat with glasses of Burgundy and looking up into each other's eyes like newly-weds. Bertie guided me around them to a cushion on the floor and asked regally, 'Goudle or Guinness, dear?' I settled for a bottle of Guinness and offered my thanks, and my host went over to a man with bright red hair and whispered something in his ear. The man's face showed annoyance and he replied quite audibly, as they both looked at me, 'I don't want him! He's all pimply anyway.' Bertie smiled and I returned his smile. The two lesbians smiled and I returned their smile. Two men who looked like builder's labourers stared contemptuously at me.

A fat man stood with Brendan in the corner of the room,

his shoulder touching the edge of a print – a naked woman with a fig leaf. They were arguing. 'You promised it to me, Brendan,' said the fat man. 'And,' said my brother, 'you'll bloody well get it!'

'I will,' said the other man bitterly, 'when it has been published by every damned magazine on the continent.' Brendan gesticulated with his hand and threw his head back to get his mouth over a stammer. 'For Christ's sake, Newman! The circulation of *Points* is not as great as the Bible in India.' Newman, very sullenly, said, 'That's all very well, Brendan, but we paid you, and we didn't expect that it should have been published elsewhere.' I knew they were discussing *Bridewell Revisited*, which had recently appeared in a French magazine and after a long life among the strap-hangers was to wind up as *Borstal Boy*. 'Anyway,' said Brendan, 'if you're goin' to spend the whole night talkin' about a bloody story I got an afternoon's drinkin' for, I'm not. I've more to do with meself.' Gently, he asked, 'Jonathan, will yeh give me a few quid to get to Paris next week.' Breathing heavily through his nostrils and tightening his lips the publisher retorted, 'I certainly will not! Where do you think I'd get it?' Brendan stared angrily into Newman's averting eyes and said, 'By jazes! but the man who said that yeh can live as long as yeh like with the rich, but when yeh make up the bill yeh'll find they'll not have spent half as much as yerself, well, he was bloody right!' Newman indignantly came to his own defence. 'Am I to be expected to keep every fellow who has a bent towards literature and art? Don't I do my share?' Brendan stood back, trembling with rage. 'Don't think of me as a fellow. The word in your kind of mouth means serf or even slave. I'm not yer lackey. "Do my share" indeed! What else are yeh fit for? Don't I know that if you could write yer name on anything but a cheque you'd never come near the likes of me! Not bloody likely! Lady Lavery's picture on a pound note only makes yeh think of the Stock Exchange. Pound notes for art! Art? Yeh spell it with a capital "F" and give me a pain in me arse! But yis buy yer way in or mammy buys it for yeh. Like our old reliable Podmore there. That's right, my little son of a multi-millionaire robber. Though you remember, Newman, that he's a cut above you because your crowd only grabbed their shekles lately. You go, and tell Daddy and Mammy Podmore that neither me nor me company is for sale. And you, Mr Editor Newman, I'm keepin' yer twenty quid as payment for listening to your views on literature, for they're nothin' short of obscene.'

'Now, now, Brendan,' began Newman conciliatingly. 'Now now, me balls,' interrupted Brendan, 'go back to Mammy now an' tell her from me the account is fuckin' closed!' Newman laughed a little nervously, Podmore joined in the laugh, but only just. Bertie swayed over from his hips and wagged a finger at Brendan. 'Now now, Brendan, I just knew you were in the naughtiest mood tonight,' and turning to Newman and Podmore he promised, 'He doesn't really mind you having a great deal of money, do you, Brendan? No, of course not. He's glad some of his friends have it instead of all those dreadful horsy people. And you *will* give him the fare for Paris, won't you, Jonathan? Of course you will. There's a dear. Now, like the good children you are, let's carry on with the party. And you, Liz, come back this instant, you can't take Kathy into the backroom yet, there are those who are there before you. Do give us a song, Ena. There's a sweetie.'

'Feather beds are soft, painted rooms are bonny,' sang Ena, and Bertie sat on the floor next to me and squeezed my hand and when I didn't react he slipped his hand below the bottom of my jacket and underneath my shirt. And I drank the remainder of my Guinness in one draught and stood to get another, and Ena, noticing my plight, sat on the floor by Bertie, whose smile for her was refrigerated. Kathy and Liz froze on me, as did the chap with the bright red hair, and the two labouring-looking men beamed and one of them came over to stand next to me at the door. 'Nancy boy, huh?'

'What do you mean?' I asked. 'Yer man there, the long fella, bit of a puff.'

'Oh,' I said, 'you think so?'

'Oh, for God's sake, don't gimme that and you after leapin' away from him like a frightened hare.' This was more embarrassing than it had been sitting beside Bertie. I don't like racialism, in race, colour, or sex. And yet my way of reacting to it always seems to imply personal cowardice in my efforts to avoid head on clashes over it. Brendan would behave differently. 'Fuck off!' he'd say, and that would be an end of it. 'Me and me mate fancy the birds in the corner, though. Joe that is. Joe Harrison. I'm Jack Nunan, work in the Corporation.' 'Lesbian,' I said. 'What's that?'

'The two women you and your friend fancy, I was sayin' they're lesbians.'

'What in the namea jazes is that?'

'They only go for women.'

'Yer kiddin'! Well, the dirty bleedin' whores! Eh, Joe, c'mere a minit. Listen to this!' As Joe approached I felt mortified and cursed my big bloody mouth. And then the basement door swung open and about ten people staggered in well armed with Guinness.

Bertie stood to greet the newcomers and staggered drunkenly. A shield, I guessed. Wearing it because of me. Jonathan Newman and Podmore were drunk too, and so was Brendan. Tomorrow they could meet and publicly forget there had ever been an angry word between them. Ena was drunk from too much drink. I was getting full and sick, and suddenly it rushed up from my neck into my mouth and I was staggering blindly after my handkerchief and Bertie was holding my head over a sink somewhere in the back and I fell asleep in a bed and didn't give a damn for Bertie or the party. Then I came alive and awake and examined myself. I was fully clothed and untouched. He's a bloody gentleman anyway.

I made my way into the narrow low-ceilinged passage at the end of which I saw a lighted room and heard the sounds of boisterous laughter and raucous song. That's where the party is. But where does he keep the bog? I listened for a moment and then heard faintly the unmistakable signal of a cistern. The sound was coming from behind me from the other end of the passage. I turned a corner and saw a shaft of light peeping from a chink in the door of what had been a wine-cellar. I pushed the door open and saw a WC bowl and the stuttering cistern above. I went back to the party, the skin of my forehead taut.

Empty Guinness bottles were stacked neatly under the window – dozens of them. Goudle was now the only drink and about eight wine bottles were passing from hand to hand as I entered the room. Brendan looked up from the conversation he was holding and remarked, 'Ah, the dead arose. . . . Now sit down and listen if yeh want to. But if not for Christ's sake go back to kip or get yourself a taxi outa *this* man's world. Well, anyway,' he went on, as Ena handed me a half bottle of Burgundy, 'this place she had up in Dorset Street – you remember it, Margaret . . .' I looked across the room and noticed Margaret Boyce, a sweet little country kid of about seventeen of whom I knew Brendan was very fond. They seemed fond of each other. She was intelligent and good-looking. Brendan was slim and very handsome. My mother had the two of them practically married from the first moment she set eyes on Margaret.

'Nice gentle girl, Brendan,' she had said, 'do be good to her.' Just now Margaret looked right enough until she spoke and then I realised she wasn't the better for drink. 'What's that, Brendan?' He hated his women to drink or mix with the company he kept. 'Mrs bastardin' Roberts that kept the jazes house in Parnell Street.' His temper was going. He tried to steady his voice and ignore the inebriation of his girl friend. 'She was a great rebel and this house she had was really someplace for any IRA man on the run. She helped to eke out her money for providing a roof for the cause by keeping at the same time a few old civil servants and other steady-going bachelors. After a while, though, it was as much as a man's neck was worth to seek refuge with the old lady. And our crowd wouldn't touch it with a barge-pole. In the heel of the hunt she became so confused that all she had to hear about a bloke was that he had been in the nick or escaped from the nick and bejazes whoever he was had a free gaff for life. Towards the end she had taken in burglars, murderers and sex maniacs. All of whom she thought were rebels who had suffered for the cause. She believed, God help her, she was building a living shrine to Republicanism, but all she was left with was a glorified brothel! Still, I suppose there are rebels in all walks of life. God be good to her, she'll be remembered longer than the creepin' jazeses who slagged her.' She would, captured for all time in *The Hostage*.

'I think it was a terrible way to deceive the old lady,' said the man with the bright red hair. 'Oh, don't feel out in the cold, Wilfred,' replied Brendan, 'there was plenty of your persuasion there too.'

'Oh, Brendan,' said Bertie, 'that wasn't very nice.'

'I should care, Bertie,' retaliated Wilfred, 'let people think what people will. I know what I am and that's that.'

'But,' laughed Brendan, 'everybody knows what yeh are, Wilfred, and nobody cares a twopenny curse.'

'Let me tell you, Brendan Behan, I went to the doctor last week for an examination and he asked me to promise to keep away from women for at least six months.'

'Ah, for Christ's sake, Wilfred, the poor man must have been demented. He meant you should keep away from men.'

'Men or women,' said a little drunk in the corner, 'celibacy is the only thing.'

'Oh, are yeh there, Arthur Daniels? Will yeh take a look at the man that's talkin' about celibacy. A Presbyterian minister that was. Went over to London, got a job with the head of a well-known publishin' house, ran away with the man's wife back to his living in Belfast, and the text of his first sermon on return was "God is love".' The Reverend Arthur Daniels stood to his full height of five four and ran out the door and up the basement steps, only waiting long enough on the pavement to shout back down the area, 'Who mocks the cloth of the Lord's anointed shall perish by the wayside.'

'Now,' said Brendan, 'there's a bloody little nut. How did he manage to see over the top of the pulpit?'

'Ah,' said Bertie, 'you were very unkind to the poor man.'

'Unkind, me arse,' replied my brother. 'It's only by makin' a mockery of other people's weaknesses we get through a fun life at all. When his first wife died he stayed devoted to her memory for ten years. Never looked sideways at another woman. Then about a year ago he asked me to go with him to Tom Daly – yeh know the sculptor fella with the studio in Leeson Street. Anyway, he had made a death-mask of Daniels' wife which Arthur had never had enough money to pay for – and yeh remember what Daly was like, wouldn't give yeh the time of day without a cheque in advance. We got into Daly's place and had to wait while he finished a job he was doin'. There was a model, and jazes she'd the best figure I'd ever seen. Big breasts throwing shadows down over her navel and her hips arched like she was gettin' ready to mount a horse. I was in a bad way. But if I was sufferin' Daniels was goin' through sheer agony. His mouth was wet, his eyes were stark. And after a few minits he walked towards Daly's jacks like a penguin goin' to the sea. He stayed there about five minutes, and when he came out he was exhausted. "C'mon, Brendan," he muttered, "let's go for a drink."

' "But," I asked, "what about your wife's death-mask."

' "No, no, Brendan," he replied, "let the dead rest. Let them rest in peace." '

'The dirty ould bastard,' said Jack Nunan when Brendan had finished.

'Oh,' Bertie replied, shocked, 'how *could* you say so! I think it was just sweet. Sweet and beautiful. Very touching.'

'Pure bloody filth,' said Nunan, 'an' the oul sculptor was worse to let outsiders run around his place when he's doin' work on someone in the nude. All them arty fellas is the same, anyway. There's no reason why they shouldn't use these models with their clothes on and then do the rest from imagination.'

'I'm glad,' said Brendan, 'that none of them are condemned to your imagination because yeh've a mind like a bloody sewer. And, as for naked models, I'm damned sure I'd sooner look at one of them with no clothes on than you in the Crown Jewels with a tiara on your cock. Even the lowest whore I've been with would be a more attractive proposition.'

'Brendan!' said Margaret, shocked. He looked at her. 'What are you on about?'

'I'll tell you,' she shouted, 'I'll tell you!' Margaret was

76

becoming quite hysterical. She started to strip, to the amazed amusement of everybody but Kathy and Liz. First her pullover. Then her skirt and petticoat and at last she stood in brassière and pants. She stood and Brendan ignored her. She moved round the room and he didn't look. She stood in front of him and he asked contemptuously: 'Well, it's naked women we're on about. Get the rest off, or haven't yeh the fuckin' guts?'

'Yes,' said Nunan, 'why don't yeh get the rest off, yeh dirty bitch.' Brendan jumped from his chair, grabbed Nunan by the lapels of his jacket, and drove his head into Nunan's face, then as Nunan lay on the ground and Brendan made to kick him I pulled his leg back and said, 'For Christ's sake, man, take hold of yourself and don't behave like a common bousey.'

'I'll bousey yeh,' he replied. I put my hand on the back of his collar and holding him tightly said, 'Don't ever try that, Brendan. I'll fuckin' kill yeh!' He sat back in his chair surprised, it was the first time I'd ever sworn in front of any member of my family.

Ena ushered the now sobbing Margaret through the door and out into the passage. Bertie and Jonathan Newman followed with the profusely bleeding Nunan. 'Speaking about naked women,' said Podmore, looking at Bertie's framed print, 'look at this one of "The Maja Nude".' 'Goya,' said Brendan from his chair, 'painted 1798 – the same year Father Murphy was burned by the bloody English at Vinegar Hill,' and he started to sing 'At Vinegar Hill O'er the Pleasant Slaney', and carried on until he wept into his wine bottle. 'But,' said Podmore, 'there's something wrong.'

'Yes,' said Bertie, coming back into the room with Mr Newman, 'it now has a fig leaf. It was added later – much later, this very year in fact. That dreadful girl did it. Didn't you, Liz?' Liz began to cry drunkenly and said, 'I couldn't stick it any longer, it was so so like my first dear friend Carol, who deserted me for a serving girl in Rathmines.'

'An',' said Brendan, 'yeh mean the fig leaf made all that difference?'

'Oh indeed,' replied Liz, 'changed her completely. There's absolutely no resemblance now. Is there, Kathy?'

'None,' said Kathy, very matter-of-fact. 'Unforgivable,' said Bertie. 'Unforgivable,' said I. 'Unforgivable,' said Podmore, and flung a Guinness bottle at the print and the glass splintered on the stone floor. Newman thought it a great game and threw a bottle. So did Kathy and Liz and everybody else, and in a little while the ground below the print was littered with broken glass over which Bertie was weeping drunkenly. 'My rent,' he wept, 'my rent, and I did mind you so well.'

'What's he on about?' I asked Brendan, who was making for the door leading to the street. 'The bottles,' he replied, 'Bertie would have made a couple of quid on the refund. That's why he holds parties at all. And you, yeh eejit, yeh couldn't even prevent that. C'mon, and we'll get home outa this. Have yeh the price of a taxi?' I said I had. 'C'mon then, before yeh break somethin' else.'

7

'Take it down from the mast Irish Traitors
The Flag we republicans claim
It can never belong to Free Staters
You've brought on it nothing but shame
But leave it to those who are willing
To uphold it in War and in Peace
The men who intend to do killing
Until England's tyranny cease.'

'WHY ARE YEH ALL DRESSED UP at this hour of the mornin'?'
asked Da, 'are yeh not goin' to your work?' We were standing outside the parlour door, and I put a finger to my lips,
bidding him speak softly. 'I'm goin' somewhere today and I
don't want the other fella to know.' My father hunched his
shoulders, as much as to say, 'Between yeh it is,' and as he
opened the hall door and the weatherboard struck the
stone step my mother came out of the kitchen and whispered, 'Don't be makin' so much noise. Poor Brendan has a
sick head.' Da laughed, and left with a glance over his
shoulder at Ma, and the valedictory, 'Poor Benjamin, while
I'm away to my nice warm work he'll have to lie all day
in that cold ould bed.'

I went back into the kitchen and, taking a roll of notes
from my back pocket, I counted four single pounds into
Ma's hand. 'There yeh are now. I don't think I owe yeh

anything. I'm goin' away for the weekend but when the other fella gets up, tell him nothin'.' 'Ah,' she said, 'poor Brendan. And him the one that loves to hear a bit of news.'

When the streets were well aired, Ma knocked on the sanctuary and whispered through the door to Brendan that breakfast was ready. 'Have yeh the paper?' he asked. 'I have,' Ma replied, 'and the nicest little mushrooms yeh ever saw.' 'Good,' said Brendan, 'I'll be there in a minute.'

'They were the curse of the famine,' he said as he sat to the table. 'What's that?' asked Ma. 'Mushrooms,' he answered. 'When yeh saw more than the usual growth in the fields then yeh knew that the potatoes had been hit. I see,' he said, looking at the paper, 'a fella has been elected on the fifteenth count. That sort of thing makes a mockery of proportional representation. Will yeh lend us a quid?'

Mother was neither shocked nor startled, but she put on a show of surprise. 'Where in the world would I get a pound on Friday mornin', Brendan? Yeh saw me yerself tryin' to make a manage on the ten shillin's I got from Tommy on me ring yesterday morning? Are yeh mad or what?' 'I heard yeh gettin' yer money from Dominic this mornin'.' She looked at him and covered up her mouth. 'Yeh could hear the grass growin'. But I've too much to do, Brendan. By the time I release Da's suit and a couple of other things there'll be little left of either of their wages.' He waved an end to the conversation. 'If yeh don't want to give it to me, that's that.'

He read silently with glances over the top of the paper at Ma. 'Nice mushrooms,' he said. Mother sat counting her debts. He read for a while. 'I'd nearly risk a famine for them, begod. Tell me, Mother, did yeh ever hear a song that goes ... The praties they grow small over here?' Unfair tactics, Ma would rather live in the workhouse than not sing. 'Don't I know every song in Ireland that was ever written? When my poor father had lost everything and we were in the shabbiest basement he used to write the songs in chalk on the wall so that we'd never forget them.' And in a big voice of her father's she loudly declaimed, ' "With a rifle as a redcoat, yer son yeh wouldn't spurn? I'd blow yer brains out on the floor, said Mick of Carrickbyrne." '

At the end of a blood-curdling account of what the Irish would do to the Saxon, in which Ma's song likened the battle to a harvesting, the Redcoats being the corn, the Fenians the Reapers, Brendan said, 'I'm goin' to pawn my typewriter, and I'll give yeh the pound off that. If not I'll pay yeh when I get the money from the "Confirmation Suit".'

'Oh,' asked Ma, 'did yeh sell that story?' 'I did, begod,' replied Brendan, 'and for good money.' 'It won't go to press as it is, will it?' Ma asked. 'Why not?' he replied. 'Well,' began my mother, 'I thought I'd remind yeh. That suit wasn't made for you, Brendan, as yeh said in the story. Don't yeh remember it was made for Rory? Sure yer Granny wouldn't allow anything on you that didn't come out of a tailor's shop. She'd have died first.' 'Ah, Mother, for Christ's sake gimme the quid and let me out of this. I've never heard such rubbish. There's not a haporth the matter with me memory. I know bloody well that the suit was made for Rory. It just makes the story better when I say it was made for me, that's all.' He looked at the clock. 'Christ!' he muttered. 'I'll be late. They'll be gone without me. Is that clock fast?' 'Right to the very minute,' said Ma. 'Maybe half an hour on but no more.' 'Who'll be gone without you?' Brendan laughed as he pulled the tie round his waist, and shoved Ma away when she tried to stuff his shirt into his pants. 'That precious little gem of yours and his cronies. If they think they're goin' to leave me here while they go to a good drinkin' county on their own . . . well.' He held up his cheek to be kissed as he took the note from her hand, then grabbing his typewriter he ran for the bus with hellos and goodbyes for all who passed.

Paddy Collins and I waited with Eddie Connell for Christie O'Neill to arrive at McDaid's. The pub opened its doors at half past ten and the manager, Paddy O'Brien, asked, 'By god, you fellas are here early enough. Not go home last night?' 'Did John Ryan leave a cheque here last night for me?' I asked, as he pulled three pints and left them to settle. 'He did indeed,' replied Paddy. 'Twenty quid. Oh, by the way, Dom,' he took me to the corner of the bar, 'yeh know there's a little . . .' I pulled him nearer and said, 'I'd sooner leave it till next week. If that's alright?' He clapped his hands and said cheerfully, 'Oh, as right as rain. Now then,' as he put up the drink, 'who's the victim?'

Brendan alighted from a No 50 bus at the corner of Westmoreland Street and made his way to Kelly's pawn office in Fleet Street. 'How much will yeh give me on me typewriter, John?' he asked. 'What yeh always get, Brendan, three quid.' 'Alright, then, give it to us.' A young, shabbily dressed woman waited on her receipt. Discreetly the man handed her the ticket and a ten-shilling note. Outside he heard her saying, 'Will yeh leave that bell alone. Can yeh not keep yer hands off anything! Mother of the Devine God but between the two of yeh I'll be up in the asylum.' Brendan took the money from the pawnbroker and shoved it into his pocket. He overtook the woman at the bottom of the stairs and smiled at her two children. 'Ah fuck it!' he said to himself, and without a word he pressed the three single notes into the woman's hand and fled back into Westmoreland Street.

'I've got the car, Dom,' said Christie O'Neill as he arrived in McDaid's. 'A nice Chev, it'll give us no trouble.' He tightened the belt of his grey overcoat, arched his back and asked, 'O.K. then. Are we right?' 'Except for Ena,' I said.

'We might as well drink a pint while we're waitin',' said Paddy Collins, 'don't be so worried, Christie, it might never happen.' 'It's not myself I'm thinking of, Paddy,' said O'Neill, 'if that was the case I'd be delighted. But if Brendan comes down to Cahirciveen and gets drunk out of his mind . . . well, it wouldn't look good.' 'Drink that,' said Eddie Connell, 'and forget about the other fella. He's not even out of bed yet. Isn't that right, Dom?' 'Oh,' I said, 'away with the fairies,' as Brendan burst through the door with Ena Murphy and demanded of me, 'Since when did I give you permission to take over my Republic?' 'Good jazes!' we intoned as one, but quite relieved.

While Brendan waited outside in the car O'Neill called the rest of us together and said, 'Now he has nothing. Not a penny. We'll buy him what drink is necessary and pay for everything else but don't let anybody give him money.' It was a sensible suggestion and we could rest happy that Brendan would be as sober as us and that would be alright as none of us drank anything stronger than Guinness. We would get to Kerry on time. We would be merry but not drunk. The oration would go off as planned and we would strike the country people as responsible Dubliners. All in all the prospect was good, very good.

'We'll stop in Portlaoghis,' said Christie as we started off. 'Portlaoghis,' cried Brendan. 'God forgive yeh, O'Neill, but that's at the other end of Ireland. We'll die of the drought.' 'Nonsense,' said Christie, 'it's no more than fifty miles.' 'Fifty miles,' sighed Brendan, 'sweet jazes but yer bein' very efficient.' 'Here, Brendan,' laughed Paddy Collins as he handed my brother a bottle of stout, 'I got a couple of dozen in case of emergencies.' 'Well, Paddy Collins,' said Brendan, 'yer blood is worth bottlin', as the oul wans say down in the market. Oh, but talkin' about the market. I was in O'Hara's the other mornin' when what yeh call him married Rita Hayworth, the Aly Khan. Well, there was two oul wans in the corner and when I say ould I really mean ancient. They must have been eighty if they were a day. One of them is gawkin' at a picture of Rita and the Prince on the front page of the Press – and a more handsome bloody man I've never seen, though I will admit I admire his taste. Anyway where was I? Oh aye, these two oul ones have a single nicotine-stained tooth between them and it waggin' away backwards and forwards as they gave the scandal full rein. One says to the other, "Messrs," she says, "how could she do it. A full-blooded woman like her to marry a blackman." "Mam," says the other oul crone, "it's beyond me thinkin', I wouldn't let a foreigner up on *me* if he'd the blessin' of St Peter himself." "No, mam," agreed the other, "not, bejazes, if his arse was studded with diamonds!" '

We had gone about twenty miles when the stout ran out and Christie said, 'We'll make one short stop in Naas so that people can use the bog.' 'Sound man,' said Brendan, 'they should make yeh president.' Then he went on to give us a lecture on the history of the town from its earliest times. 'Nas no Roig,' he said, 'the resting place of the kings, and the garrison crowd round here have to abbreviate it to "Naas" did yeh ever hear the likes.' 'No respect,' said Christie, 'but good men came outa this place too, Brendan.' 'True enough, a stoir, but I don't think the town was sacked half enough. That is, until we sacked it.' 'When was that?' asked Connell. 'After they ran Sam Nolan out of here for bein' a red. We were comin' back in '37 – I was a chissler at the time. During the row over the Republican congress, yeh remember, Christie?' 'I do well,' said O'Neill, 'I'd an uncle round at that time.' 'I knew him well,' said Brendan. 'Jack?' 'That's right,' said Christie. 'Anyway,' Brendan went on, 'we were comin' back from Bodenstown in lorries when we got the news that Sam had been thrown out of his hometown. And we made a deliberate detour through Naas and bejazes we broke every shop window and house in that place. The natives thought the Tans were back. But by Christ they'll think twice in future before they throw anyone else out.'

I don't think there is anything worse than to sit in a pub and while people around you are busy ordering drinks to be unable to stand your own shout, so I winked at Brendan to follow me to the lavatory and, when I was sure I couldn't be seen, handed him a couple of quid. 'Don't let the others know I gave yeh that or yeh'll get me killed.' 'Yer secret with me, oul son, is as safe as the grave. In fact all yer secrets are as safe.' 'How d'ye mean?' I asked. 'D'ye think now it's only yerself has the generous heart,' he replied, and taking from his hip pocket a roll of notes he said, 'They all gave me a few quid on condition I'd say nothin' about it. Jazes,' he said, 'there's top rebel security for yeh.' That tore the bottom out of things and there wasn't much of the evening left when we loaded ourselves back into the car and staggered away from inhospitable Naas.

In Portlaoghis we visited the Dublin Bar owned by Paddy McLogan and it seemed, as Brendan ordered a fiddler to play his favourite tune 'The Blackbird' for the twentieth time, my brother was more wealthy than the whole lot of us put together. 'There's a fella I know down here,' said Brendan, 'by the name of Mercy McManus and he had a little bit of a hotel. Well, one day I was racin' along in Podmore's car when we passed the bould Mercy sittin' at his door. Pull in here quick, says I to Podmore, for there's a fella we could have the best diversion with. "Mercy," says I, "will yeh come to Dublin for the weekend, oul Podmore's mother is after shootin' a few peasants and got the insurance money, so we could have a good time." "I will, Brendan," said Mercy, not even givin' a shrug of surprise that I should come across him fifty good miles from me native land, "but wait till I collect together me literature." Well now, literature, I ask yeh, the same Mercy McManus wouldn't be able to distinguish between ladies and gents if he saw them on a lavatory wall. "Go back," says I, "Mercy, and collect whatever it is yeh have" – I was thinkin' maybe it was some sort of an instrument or somethin' that he called be the name "literature" for want of somethin' better. But, as true as God's me judge, out he came from the house with a big bag of paperbacks and throws them into the rear seat beside him. "Are yeh right then, Mercy?" says I. "I am," says he, "lovely." Away we started and after a while I noticed that people were givin' us funny looks and I says to Podmore, "Would yeh ever mind takin' off that deerstalker hat, for yer makin' a show of us respectable people. Everybody in the bloody country has a glance for us." Well, it wasn't the hat, I can tell yeh that. After a bit I looked behind and what d'ye think the bould Mercy was doin'? He was tearin' out the middle two pages of each paperback between which he had concealed a fiver. He got to Dublin and he had five hundred quid so that he must have started with one hundred books. By the time he was finished strewin' the countryside with paperbacks I can tell yeh this, the stretch of road between here and Dublin must be the most well read in the country. "There's money in literature, Mercy," I says to him one time. "There is begod, Brendan, but for jazes' sake don't tell the wife!" '

It was late when we stopped at a pub in a town called Farranfomair, not too far from our destination, Cahirciveen, but Brendan was still talking away with a story for every village and a quip to match every face. He was putting on weight now, in fact he was fat. 'Oh sweet Jesus,' he'd say, looking at his legs daily disappearing under an ever growing promontory of flesh, 'I'm goin' to be like me father. When I was a child the neighbours used to look at me and say, "Ah, God love him, but he's the image of his daddy," and I'd run to the mirror and examine my mouth to see if me teeth were all there, and my head to make sure I'd still me fair share of hair. If I go bald and gummy I'll die. If I get pot-belly I'll die twice. Eena, my eena, tell me I'm still slim and eligible.' 'There's a sweetie now, Brendan. Indeed if you have a little bit of weight you'll lose it on your next sojourn in prison.' 'Oh no, Ena. Let me be fat.' 'Yeh were a fit man in the Camp, Brendan,' said Christie. 'I was that,' replied Brendan, 'but I was a bloody thirsty one. Doesn't John Joe come from around here?' he added, a thought striking him. 'He does,' said Christie, 'from Tralee, but we're not next door to him.' 'A pity,' said Brendan, 'I'd love to see him, for a more decent man never walked. He was our O/C in the Camp, Eddie.' 'Oh, I've met John Joe Sheehy,' said Eddie. 'The Kerry footballer yeh mean?' 'Aye, told me to go on hunger strike one time. But I said it was more food I wanted, not less. Never could argue Ireland's politics on the anti-Napoleonic philosophy that an army marches to heaven on its stomach. God, but the Kerry crowd were great men:

> ' 'Twas Kerry here and Kerry there, 'twas Kerry
>   Kerry everywhere
> And all across the midnight air there rang the
>   war cry Kerry!'

Brendan sang about fifteen blood-curdling verses about how the Kerry men beat the Black and Tans and ran them out of the kingdom, and in a moment we were practically saturated in free drink by the delighted villagers. We were all very drunk now except Christie, who had to keep his wits about him, and Paddy Collins who wasn't one the drink ever affected much anyway. Ena sang sweetly in her sweet voice and was quite indignant that the neighbours should take her for an English person. And Brendan said that if she was an English person, which she wasn't, it didn't make any difference to him because he had seen decent people to come from England with the exception of Prison Officers, Governors, Lawyers, Policemen, Prime Ministers and hangmen. 'I saw Pierrepoint twice,' he said, 'once in Walton Jail in Liverpool, and again when he came to top Barney Kirwan in Mountjoy. Remember that fella, Christie?' 'I do, Brendan, cut his brother up like a pig and fed him to the pigs.' 'Of course,' said Brendan, 'he didn't deserve to be hanged. A nut he was. Complete nut. But then accordin' to their own law a man should not hang if he's not responsible for what he does by reason of insanity. They had him examined by a trickcyclist. Trickcyclist how are yeh! Should have come to me. I'd have told them. He used to ask the screw to get me to sing for him so that he'd hear a nice young voice when he was goin' for the long drop. So bloody gentle. And yet he carved his brother up. One screw told me that on the mornin' of his execution Kirwan took up a glass of water and balanced it on the back of his hand saying, "There's nerves for yeh. From a man that's on his way to his Maker." And they said he wasn't potty! I've written a play about it. And I hope someone has the sense to do it, called, it was, what we used to call him. Nobody ever likes to refer to a condemned man by name; sticks in the throat; used to call him the quare fella.' 'In the camp you were calling it *The Twisting of Another Rope*,' said Christie. 'Yes,' said Brendan, 'in jail the deed of hanging, the act is the enemy. Outside, yeh can think of the victim.'

When Christie tired, Eddie took the wheel from Farranfomair and criticised the poor signposting of Irish roads all the way to Cahirciveen. At one point he turned right and cursed a sheep track that led to a barbed wire fence. 'Now there's a place to put a bloody road,' he growled. We got out of the car and looking over a gate, were rewarded with a splendid view of Dingle Bay lying all of two hundred feet below us, a sheer drop from the other side. 'A pity yeh didn't bring a pair of oars with yeh, Eddie,' said Brendan, 'we could have gone right out to the Blaskets and seen for ourselves what was so important about them as to inspire Maurice O'Sullivan's *Twenty Years a Growing*.' I felt sick with shock but the rest of the company took the near escape philosophically. 'Valentia is out there on the left, Brendan,' said Ena, 'as children in school, the priest used to tell us how the name came from Spain. Then he would go on about the Spanish influence around the south and south-west coast.' 'Well,' replied Brendan, 'I hope for the sake of his soul and the souls of all the departed from Kerry the poor man knew more about theology or is it theosophy, than he did about the origin of place names, because Valentia is pure Gaelic, meaning, the mouth of the island, "Beal na Inse".' 'Oh,' said Ena, 'I was only telling you what the priest said.' 'He said more than his prayers, my love. Still I'm glad of one thing.' 'Yes, Brendan?' asked Ena. 'I'm glad we're not floating around in that bay because the only thing Spanish about her is the Gulf Stream which hits her on the way from Mexico and hot water can get terrible fuckin' cold when it has all of four thousand miles to travel before it gets to your bath.' 'James Joyce tells us that all Ireland is washed by the Gulf Stream,' I said. 'Oh, are yeh there, Hannen Swaffer?' remarked Brendan. 'We've all read Paddy Swift's copy of *Ulysses*, yeh know.' 'I think,' said Christie, 'it's about time we were getting a wash ourselves in Cahirciveen.'

In Murphy's Hotel we were greeted by two big mountainy

men who received Christie like the most important VIP around the town. A man called Mikie Neill came and so did a man called Sean McNeill and when I remembered that Christie O'Neill was here to do an oration for Maurice O'Neill I thought there must be nobody of any other name in the whole county. However, we were then brought off to a house in the town by a man known as Long Johnny, who promised us drink galore for as long as we could stick it. Christie stayed behind with his mountainy friends, while Ena, Eddie, Paddy, Brendan, and I followed Long Johnny down into a room dropping from the main street. It was lit badly by an oil lamp, and all we could appreciate were the glasses and whiskey bottles offered us, and then only in Braille as it were, the contours being familiar. Johnny offered Brendan a sandwich and my brother said he'd rather not as it contained ham. 'I was on a boat last month for Le Havre on my way to Paris – I had to go direct from Cork on the American *Washington* because my English deportation order didn't allow me to go from Southampton. When we were about three miles off Le Havre an old French geezer in a beret took a snuff-box from his pocket, just as I, standing beside him, took a ham sandwich from a steward. Well, I've always been one for the customs of people – a great lover of tradition – so I was enchanted to see this old citizen throw the contents of his box into the sea. Now if the sea was his intended goal he made one mistake, instead of flinging the stuff *with* the wind he threw it *into* the wind. Result. It all comes back over me and me ham sandwich. "That's a strange rite," I said to this gas oul character, chewin' a fleshy bit of the pig as I spoke. "Do they do that all the time where you come from?" "Do vot, monsieur?" he asked. "Offer tributes to the sea," I replied. "The sea, monsieur, tributes? I no understand." I grabbed the box from his hand and gave a demonstration of what he was doing. *"Marin! Lancement!"* I screamed at the poor fella – yeh know the way people are inclined to shout when they think a foreigner is deliberately trying to misunderstand you. "Oh," he said, "Papa. *Mon père?* That was Daddy, at least a little bit of Daddy. We, what you say, burned? Cremated him, and he loved *marin*, the sea, so much we decided to throw a bit of him into her. See?" I saw. "Mister," says I, "unless yer oul fella was a cannibal yeh'd better set them to work on me with a stomach pump because bejazes ye've thrown more than a bit of *him* into me, and the cursea God on you and him, I'll never be able to eat another ham sandwich as long as I live." '

We sat on the edge of what I had believed to be a wooden packing case, and it was only when the first light of dawn had taken over from the oil lamp did we realise our seat was a nearly completed coffin. I rose nervously and Long Johnny said, 'Yerrah, is it afraid yeh are of an ould soddin' box? 'Tis sort of privileged yeh'd be to be makin' an armchair of Padin Mike's last sofa. Terrible well-respected man he was about these parts! Solid! Down-to-earth creature that never spent a penny but on what was necessary. Drove around on Sundays on a bicycle made for two – some say he got wed to Noreen so as not to waste the back seat. He'd dress up in overalls on the Sabbath to protect the navy blue suit he had given him by Father Nash's housekeeper in 1926. Not a break on it, no more nor him. Saw him at the wake. Might as well have been asleep. Oh 'tis a most respectable man's house yer sittin' on now.' 'Joyce says an Irishman's home is his coffin,' said Brendan. 'Yes,' replied Long Johnny, 'and if Noreen Mike doesn't put up her price for the funeral her husband will never cross the threshold to warm his arse in this one.'

'I dare say you've seen a good many off, Johnny?' asked

Brendan. Long Johnny smiled for a second, stroked his chin thoughtfully, and said, 'Since the business came to meself when me Da went under in 1910, I'd have mailed a parish and a half down below to the black fella.' Brendan laughed and said, 'D'ye not think one or two of yer customers might have gone upstairs?' ' 'Tis a question,' replied Johnny, 'was asked of me Christmas twelvemonths when came the turn of Tommy the Polis to be planted. A most miserable man, may the Lord have mercy on his soul, if the Lord would have any truck with the likes. Left all his money to the Church and not a halfpenny for a wet for his wake. Oh, the clergy had reason for a good cry, two hundred sovereigns of the best of good reason, but meself and Ned the Grave came back from Cahirciveen churchyard as dry as a nun under a habit. On the way home Father Nash says to me, "Ah well, Long Johnny, if ever a man was in heaven this minit it's Tommy the Polis." "Beggin' yer pardon, Father," says I, "but I've as much knowledge of funerals as yerself, havin' been the strong right arm of many an unwillin' traveller from around here, and all I can say is that if Tommy the Polis is in heaven this minit he'll be the first one in my time from this parish." '

When Long Johnny's whiskey dried up at five in the morning we repaired to the hotel. Paddy, Eddie, and I went straight to bed. Ena and Brendan cajoled the hotel proprietor out of his rest and when we rose again some four hours later the two of them were quite drunk, Ena with a glass of gin and Brendan talking thickly over a tumbler of whiskey. Christie came down looking fit and well and ready for the oration, but when he saw Brendan's condition his face became a mask of near despair. 'What in God's name are we going to do now, Eddie?' he asked. 'I was just thinking about that,' said Eddie, 'we can't take him to the cemetery as he is now but if we go without him he'll raise murder.' 'Maybe we could get something to send him to sleep for a while,' suggested Paddy. 'A good idea,' Eddie agreed. 'I'll go and see a chemist friend of mine and I'll get some sort of a Micki for him.' Eddie was advised by his chemist friend to put the sleeping draught in a glass of gin where it would not be noticed. 'What the hell is this?' demanded Brendan very drunkenly. 'A drop of gin,' said Eddie, 'just to fix you up.' 'Who *wants* to be fixed up?' shouted Brendan, 'and not on that bloody mother's ruin anyway.' 'Sure it's mine, Brendan pet,' said Ena, and before we could stop her she drained the glass and slept soundly for about twelve hours.

The two mountainy men came to collect Christie for the oration and Paddy went with him. Eddie looked up as they left and said, 'We'll follow later.' Brendan stirred and demanded, 'When are they comin' back for us?' I ordered another drink and he was quiet again but for an occasional snatch of a song with which he slowly became quite pre-occupied, 'Sweet Kerry fair was far from where they murdered brave O'Neill.' 'We can't leave him out of the funeral,' said Eddie. 'But we must,' I replied, 'for everybody's sake we must. If he gets near the cemetery in the condition he is now we'll never live it down. Besides, it's not fair to Christie.' 'Dominic,' said Eddie, 'I know how Brendan feels. He didn't come here for the trip. He came to sorrow over somebody he really loved. He was *inside* when they executed Maurice. If he takes a drink now it's only like holding a postponed wake.' 'You go ahead, Eddie, I'll stay here.' Brendan stood with tears in his eyes and whispered, 'You skinny little fucker! You creepin' jazes. What do you know of a man's feelings? Who the hell ever gave you the right to judge whether a man is fit company for the dead. I felt that man's death with a physical pain. Oh Christ! What would you know?' I had to be sure conventions were observed — we mustn't allow anybody to disgrace us, not even a man who had heard an execution from a prison cell because, as he said in *Brendan Behan's Island*, 'I couldn't very well help it; it happened within a hundred yards of me, and it seems that all the rifles were loaded.'

8

'Some can drink and still keep sober
Some can fight and no get slain
I can sleep wi' another man's lass
And still be welcome tae ma ain.'

RORY AND I WERE ALWAYS LOOKED UPON by my father as being
somewhat odd. Harmless, mind you, but odd. And when
he heard we intended to start up in the painting business as
contractors he remarked, 'That's a fine brand of political
warfare for Socialists. Unusual. I mean the idea of taking
over the bottom from the top. Most of the other ones used
to like doing it the other way.' I cut him short and asked,
'All we want you to do is grain a few hall doors in your
spare time. We'll pay yeh for the work.' He took the pipe
from his mouth and said, 'You won't have a helluva lot
left for me when you've paid the other fella.' 'What are yeh
on about?' I asked. 'Brendan,' he replied. 'Who said anything about employing him?' asked Rory. 'Well, nobody as
yet, but yeh'll find that yer mother's tongue is a far harder
cross to bear than yer brother. I've been married to her for a
long time now and I often feel it might be a relief to spend
a couple of months on a crucifix.' 'If that fella comes near
our job,' I told Da, 'I'll have him arrested.'

On Monday morning Brendan arrived on the site at half
past eight on the dot. He took a ragged white bib-and-brace
from a newspaper and said, 'That's the only costume I
have, but wait. Just wait. They say industry is its own

reward, but,' and he winked at me, 'we know that the reward of industry itself is not enough. Oh, it's a great sort of feelin'. The freedom of it! Startin' to toil for your own, and not to be exploited by every rack-rentin', slave-drivin' employer in the country.'

Rory beamed and said, 'I'll say this for yeh, Brendan, yeh show great eagerness to be here right on time to start work.' 'I do that, Rory. And if it wasn't for the appointment I have in the *market* at half past nine, nothin'd do me better than to get stuck into it with yeh. But always remember, Rory, when God made time he made a lot of it. There's always tomorrow.' A quid from Rory and he was gone. I fumed, Rory laughed and said, 'I wonder when we'll see him again.'

Three weeks passed and with no sign of Brendan I began to entertain hopes that he had taken up residence on the Left Bank permanently. I was further encouraged in this belief by the fact that, prior to his disappearance, he had been heard to quote frequently Joyce's line about 'silence, exile, and cunning'. I nearly choked on a pint of Guinness when I saw Podmore and he reflected in the mirror of McDaid's.

'Oh,' I asked, 'are yeh back?' 'From where?' he wanted to know. 'From wherever yeh've been,' I replied. 'I could have been hidin' down in the lavatory for all you know. And if I came up out of there yeh'd hardly ask me if I was back. When yeh don't know where a person has been yeh then don't know if he has come back.' And he turned to the general company and said, mimicking a young, high-pitched voice, 'Oh, yer back are yeh? Yeh've been away have yeh? Would they not keep yeh wherever yeh were if yeh were there at all.' And in his own voice he appealed to the Ginger Man sitting in the corner of the bar, 'In the name of jazes, Gainor, did yeh ever hear the likes? Of course I'm

Brendan, his father and mother, and brother Dominic.

Brendan Behan sleeps through a rehearsal of Dominic's play *Posterity Be Damned,* pictured next to his mother and father.

Beatrice, Brendan's widow, and Dominic at Brendan's funeral, 1963. Playwright John B. Keane is far right.

Mr and Mrs Stephen Behan at Brendan's graveside.

back,' he said, turning to me, 'what other condition could I be in when yer lookin' at me from the only two eyes yeh have.' 'I was making an observation,' I said, and my voice sounded young and effeminate, 'I was not askin' a question.' 'Well,' he replied, 'I won't say but that yer observant. Behold,' he instructed the company, 'the observer! Podmore, give Galileo here a suitable trophy. Give him yer oulfella's racing binoculars.'

Gainor Crist sat, a man of function, in his sports jacket, grey flannel pants, and bow tie. Somebody would have had to tell you that the feet nestling under the high stool were shod in plimsoles. He was not amused by Brendan's display. Not because of me. Because he thought it unnecessary. We are not easily amused, I thought, looking then from Crist to Brendan.

'How is the smuggling, Brendan?' asked Crist. 'Didn't do any,' said my brother, 'a bit too bloody dangerous at the moment.' Crist laughed into himself and said, 'I didn't think danger would worry you if the entertainment was good?' 'It ceases to be funny when they start carving each other up and distributin' the bits all over England from an aeroplane,' replied Brendan. 'I don't mind fightin' the British Army, Gainor, but some of them fellas in Soho are really vicious.' 'I thought they'd be friends of yours,' suggested Crist. 'Too bloody true,' replied Brendan, 'wouldn't I be the right oul eejit to have them for enemies?'

McDaid placed a half-pint of stout in front of the Ginger Man and as the latter took some silver from his side pocket and examined it under the counter Brendan told Podmore, 'Get that drink on our round. Make it a pint, Gainor?' he asked. 'This will do just fine,' said the latter, and enquired, 'Now that you're back from wherever you've been, Brendan, would you mind telling me where my bloody fiver is that I loaned to you for one hour, three weeks ago?' 'But you owed me one,' said Brendan. 'Don't change the subject,' warned Gainor, 'the one I loaned you was food money.' 'I'm sorry,' said Brendan, 'I didn't know the difference. Here, Podmore, lend's a fiver for a second.' 'What do you mean by a second, Brendan?' asked Podmore. 'Well,' replied Brendan, 'as long as it takes for you to pass it to me and me to pass it to him. We'll time it if you're so bloody particular.' He laughed and said, 'Though why I should be giving fivers to a man with an income from Uncle Sam is beyond me. Can anybody join the Yankee Army for a free education in Trinity or is it only ones that were born on the sod?' Gainor looked up as Mr McDaid lifted Podmore's fiver from the counter and said, 'Thank yeh, Mr Eh eh, that'll be only one left on the bill now, but there was no need to worry. Time enough!'

Mr McDaid snapped the till shut and Gainor said regretfully, 'Put money in thy purse. That's the trouble with manners. I didn't want to pick it up at once because it's such bad form.' 'Just as well, Gainor,' said Brendan, 'because if the Yanks get to hear yer spendin' their all-American money on drink and reds yeh'll lose the "Purple Heart" they gave yeh for crossing the Atlantic, or is it the Pacific they dish them out for?' 'They say desk generals have been honoured for crossing Times Square under acute ticker-tape fire,' said Gainor, 'but don't try to amuse me now, Brendan. I'm too distressed.' 'I'm sorry for yer trouble, sir,' said Brendan, and to Podmore he added, 'Damn you, man, can you not remove your hat and show some respect?'

A man in riding britches entered, his wife on his arm. She sat beside the fire and he went to the counter, jostling Brendan as he made his way. 'I do beg your pardon, sir?' he pleaded in an upper-class accent, and Brendan, slipping into the character of the latter replied, 'My pardon, sir, shall ever be yours to do with whatever you might propose.'

The man laughed and said, 'Well said, sir. Jolly well said.'
Then, noticing Podmore, he exclaimed, 'Osbert, my boy!
How nice to see you. Saw your dear father out riding this
morning. Hope to see him to hounds on Saturday.' 'Yes,
Major,' said Podmore. 'Well, be the Lord God, Podmore,
are there many more at home like him?' asked Brendan.
'He's a friend of Daddy's,' replied Podmore. 'At his age I'd
hardly expect him to be a school chum of yours. What does
he do?' Brendan asked. 'He's Master of the foxhounds out
our way. I think they also have a little place in Limerick.
Major Denver-Denver.' 'Well,' said my brother, 'I can detect
the waste of at least one Denver. And it further shows that
the man has no confidence in his ability to make himself
understood if he wants people to go around referring to
him twice.' 'Imagine how posterity will deal with their
children. "Ah yes, dear, dear, and you are one of the
Denver-Denver-Denvers who are now, unfortunately,
quite gone. Dreadful accident, spilt his hyphens into a
lavatory bowl at a hunt ball. Don't you remember his balls?
He held his balls for hours after a hunt."' 'Yeh know,
Podmore, yeh belong to a vulgar race when yer connected
to a crowd like that.' 'They're amusing, at any rate, and if
they choose to spend their weekends chasing dogs, well, it's
a pardonable type of lunacy,' said Gainor. 'If yeh were to
buy them for fools,' said Brendan, 'yeh'd be gettin' a damn'
bad bargain. They amble around this country almost anony-
mously, bein' liked and respected as quaint and queer, but
decent, decent mind yeh, poor gentlemen. Butter would
hardly melt in their mouths to look at them. And yet
they're the children and grandchildren of murderin' Lords
bastards and cut-throats who bled this very country white
until they were forced to get out at the point of a gun. And
they changed their mailed suits for Donegal Tweed of the
finest cut, and their swords for cheque books and got back

the family estate with the stroke of a pen. What have they
lost? Nothing but the hatred of the people. They have all
they want and more and behind every grin of a "good
morning" they hide their dislike of us and their delight in
our failures because all their money is in the city of London
ready to buy a whip or a cage in whatever part of the world
their gilt edge happens to be invested at the moment.'
'You don't agree then that the Anglo/Irish eventually
become more Irish than the Irish themselves?' asked
Gainor. Brendan thought for a moment and said, 'I think
yeh probably had in mind the Normans. That was a long
time ago, Gainor. Anyway, there's no such animal as the
Anglo/Irishman or what I call the "Angst". A bloke is
either Irish or not Irish. It hasn't got much to do with where
yeh were born; as my mother says, "because yeh were born
in a stable doesn't make yeh a horse". Shaw was of English
stock, but like Yeats' people so many generations back it
made no matter. On the other hand, Congreve was born
in Ireland and trained as a lord's steward and claimed to be
English and said he was born in England; since his thought
is English and for England he might as well belong to them.
But, and this is the important bit, nobody has ever accused
Congreve of being Anglo/*English*. The Anglo kick was
probably invented by the English to prohibit a recurrence
of the Norman carry-on when a whole invading army was
eaten together with their heritage and shit out in a progeny
of Irishry – indomitable Irishry, W. B. called them. There are
Russian Jews who got out of their country into England
before the revolution and are hardly a generation removed
from Russia and they are accepted by all as English or at
worst British. The Anglo/*Englishman* doesn't exist because
people in high places decide not to have any. Being
British is another trick of the tweedy men, otherwise Lloyd
George becomes Anglo/English, so does Ramsay Mac-

Donald and Christ yeh'd have the best of sport when it came to the descendants of Charlie Stuart, further complicated by boudoir associations with Germany, Greece, and Russia. The English claim Yeats, but not Parnell, Wilde but not Pearse, and they wouldn't give you tenpence for Casement or Childers, but offer them Synge, Swift, and Goldsmith and they'd dance the walls of Limerick. The Yeats, Shaws, etcetera, live in Ireland as Irishmen and face the problems Irishmen have to face. The horsy crew bank in English and think in English. They think of us as John Bull's other island, as Shaw said. Not, mind yeh, Podmore, that I'd say one word against the likes of you, for I'd nearly swear your oul wan fell into a hedge with an Irish gardener before you were born. But to hell with that rubbish! Guess where we've been?' asked Brendan. 'Ah, I'll take yeh outa yer misery; we've just returned from the land of the Sassenach. Would yeh believe that?' 'I thought you were liable to imprisonment if you returned to England?' asked Gainor. 'Aye,' said Brendan, 'but if you knew the English police. El Cid, as they call the CID. They wouldn't catch a virgin in a nunnery. Yeh may laugh, but as true as God's me judge I've not only been in the capital of the Empire for three weeks but I've visited a court, a police station, and a prison. Isn't that right, Podmore?' With a nod Podmore corroborated and Brendan went on, 'I've had the gassest diversion imaginable. Yeh see, Podmore's cousin is married to this one, what's her name?' 'Firna,' said Podmore. 'And, of course, I fancy her. We're stoppin' in the place for a few days. The husband and wife in the front room and meself an' yer nibs here in the back. This nut of a husband, what's this his name is?' 'Cedric,' said Podmore. 'He gets up in the middle of the night in his skin, nothin' on but the light, as they say. He looks over at the window in his room and declares, "Firna, somebody is trying to gain entrance."

Not, mind yeh, somebody tryin' to jazes well break in. Gain entrance, how are yeh. Up he gets with a big carvin' knife and away down the street bollocks naked after this other fella. In a minute his wife comes in and says to me, "Get up quickly and follow Cedric. He's gone down the road after a man and I fear he'll do him an injury. He's gone out stark naked." Well, up I jumps and am outside the door before I realise that I'm naked too. Now what in the name of God would anybody think to see one nude man chase another on the public highway in the early hours of the morning? So I slipped back into the house, locked the door, and crept upstairs and sat under a landin' window watchin' the road.' 'Why did yeh lock the door?' asked Gainor. 'Well, by that time the little Machiavellian streak had risen in me and apart from wantin' to see the fun I thought if I could keep the other fella from gettin' back I'd have every opportunity for knockin' off Firna. I knew they wouldn't be able to hear the front door because they were in the back of the house.' 'You're a right bastard,' said Gainor. 'Be that as it may,' Brendan continued, 'by the time Cedric gained the end of the street – as he would say – his prey ran straight into the arms of two big polismen who would be ready to contain the field of any runnin' man at such an hour. They had their notebooks and pencils at the ready when they perceive a naked runnin' man. Cedric, realising that this was no place for a nocturnal naturist, turned in flight and ran back to the house hotly pursued by the forces of law and order.' 'To find,' said Gainor, 'that the door was locked.' 'Well, jazes, I thought I'd die laughin'. He stood lookin' at the hall door not believin' it could be shut. Then he banged on it, but the only one to hear him was meself. In a minute the two policemen come into the garden after him and bejazes I'd swear but he tried to look nonchalant. Did yeh every try to look nonchalant with no clothes on, Gainor?'

'Not lately,' replied Crist. 'The biggest of the policemen,' Brendan went on, 'took off his overcoat and put it around Cedric. Then he turns to the other fella and says, "Come on, Joe, and we'll phone a patrol car from the corner of the street." As they left with the strugglin' nude I went downstairs, opened the door and banged it to make people think I was comin' in and said to Firna, "They're after arrestin' yer husband, love. I did what I could but they've taken him off." Well, I never knew anyone to take it so cool. "In the morning," says she, "I'll have to take him some clothes, the silly man." Well, says I to myself, if that's the case, yeh might have a chance, Brendan. And indeed when all was said and done I spent a most enjoyable night or the rest of what was left of it.' 'Christ,' said Gainor, 'but you should be burned.' 'Oh,' said Brendan, 'burn me as much as yeh like but do me the courtesy of listenin' to the rest of the story.' 'D'ye not think that's enough?' asked Gainor. 'Lord,' said Brendan, 'sure I'm only beginning. In the mornin' before I've time to drink my first glass of Cedric's brandy I'm required to bring Cedric's clothes down to the station. I forgot why you didn't go, Podmore.' 'I had to go to the bank, Brendan,' says the latter. 'Oh aye, that's right, a most important function too, as Oliver Cogarty said when Davy Byrne the publican bought him a drink, "They also stand who only serve and wait." As I get to the police station I can hear a geeser speaking to a telephone and saying, "We'll just do him for the old indecency lark . . . right then, ten o'clock this morning, Marlborough Street. Cheerio then." Before he turned to me I knew he was talking about Cedric. "I've brought some clothes for Cedric," says I, and as true as jazes I didn't yet even know his second name. "Toodle," says he, "your naked friend will be done – I mean tried – at court number one at ten o'clock this morning. Just leave those clothes you brought with me an'

I'll let 'im 'ave 'em after he's done with the trickcyclist."
"Thank you," said I, and added, "How do you think he'll
get on?" The police sergeant stroked his chin and said
thoughtfully, "Oh, if it's 'is first offence and 'e gets 'imself a
lawyer 'e'll get off wiv a caution, I should imagine." "A good
lawyer?" I suggested. "Any sort of bleedin' lawyer. Yer see,
the old legal beagles on the bench sort of take it very badly
if the defendant don't get some sort of eagle to speel for
them. Shows lack of faith in the profession like." "And," I
asked, "if he doesn't get a lawyer?" "Oh," said the sergeant
with a shrug, "a month, I should think." "Thank you,"
said I. "Do you think I could see him now?" The sergeant
was hesitant and I let a pound note fall to the floor and the
sergeant smiled. "Well, I suppose it'll be alright for a few
minutes, in there, sir," and he indicated a door to my left.
I bowed, picked up the pound note, and waved it back into
me pocket.

'I passed a bearded old man in a long white coat who had
just come from the station cell in which Cedric was tem-
porarily incarcerated and heard the bearded man whisper
to a young policeman, "A sad case. A sad, sad case. And so
young, so very young. All the symptoms of GPI with a
tendency to paranoia. No hope. No hope, I'm afraid,
especially when they fail to recognise everyday things and
phenomena." The young policeman noticed me and asked,
"Anything I can do for you, sir?" "I'm looking for Mr Cedric
Toodle," and, as the young officer appeared to waver, "It's
alright, I have permission to talk with him for a few
minutes." "OK then, sir, this way. But I'll have to stay with
you in case he becomes violent." "That'll be alright," said
I, as with a clanging of keys and a grinding of heavy door-
hinges the policeman led the way into Cedric's new home.'
'Nothing new for you, Brendan,' said Gainor.

'With a blanket round his shoulders and a scowl on his

face, Cedric sat in the middle of the cell floor looking like an angry Buddhist monk contemplating a picture of the Pope. "Oh, Brendan," he cried, "thank God you've come! There are a lot of lunatics running around here shouldn't be outside the walls of London Zoo. I was beginning to think I had gone quite mad – did you see a bearded fellow in a long white coat out there just now?" I nodded my awareness of the recent presence of the gentleman so described. "Well, he's positively the most insane. He sat beside me here on the floor as though we were both going to have Japanese high tea together and says, 'Ah, Mr Toodle – or you won't mind if I calls you Cedric?' – a chap I've never met before – then he took out a notebook and pencil and started to write. After a while he said to me, 'Tell me, Cedric, do you often do this?' 'Do what?' I asked him. 'Walk around the town naked in the early hours of the morning.' 'Oh yes,' I replied, sarcastically, 'I do it on the thirty-first of every month.' 'And,' he asks like a fool, 'how do you occupy yourself in the months when there are only thirty or less days?' 'Then,' I replied, 'I have to be content to do my perambulations on the thirty-second,' and good Lord when I said that he started writing like a blasted woodpecker and all the time saying to himself, 'Oh a sad case, a very sad case.' Then he asks me, 'Cedric, if I had a pound note in that hand and a penny in this, and I offered you the choice of either, which would you take?' 'I suppose,' said I, 'I'd be damned sensible enough to take the penny.' Well, away he goes again, hell for leather across the notebook until, by jove, I thought his hand would fall off. Anyway, the last question he asked was, 'Cedric, what season of the year is this?' I took one look out through the cell window at the falling snow and I answered, 'Summer!' and with a big hurrah I let down my blanket and shouted, 'Why do you think I'm going around naked?' After that he left me, and he muttering to himself, 'A sad case, a sad, sad case.' "

'I chuckled softly to myself and said, "I brought your clothes, Cedric." "Good," he replied, "where have you put them?" "They're with the station sergeant, he'll bring them in when you're ready to go to court." Cedric sat on the edge of the bunk and asked, "How do you think I'll get on, Brendan? I mean, can they make much of a case like this?" "Not at all," said I, "as simple, I'd say, as being arrested on a charge of drunk and disorderly . . . nothing to it, I'd say a fine of five shillings would see everything straight. Though, on the other hand, it might be twenty shillings; certainly nothing more. Go into court and make a joke of it – I know that's what I'd do." Cedric's face brightened considerably. "Oh, that's wonderful consolation. I was getting very worried over maybe having to do seven days. They wouldn't do that, would they?" Said I, "If there's one thing I can assure you of, Cedric, it won't be seven days you'll get." "I suppose I should get a lawyer, though – just for seeing things straight like?" "A lawyer!" I stared at him as though he were really insane. "Do you want to get six months, man? Now listen to me," I cautioned quietly, "keep these blokes right out of a thing like this. You know what happened to a friend of mine that was charged with sitting down on an unemployment march? In fact he was really sitting on O'Connell Bridge feeding the seagulls when he was surrounded by people carrying placards and banners and singing 'We shall not be moved', so being an Irishman he joined in the chorus:

'We shall not be moved, we shall not be moved, we
    shall not be moved, we shall not be moved
Like a tree that's planted by the water we shall not
    be moved.'

"Before he knew where he was four policemen were carrying him feet first into a waiting Paddy wagon and he was up before the judge pleading not guilty. Everyone else said guilty and got off with a fine of forty shillings, but he had his lawyer to fight the case and the judge said, 'If this fellow is not guilty why would he bring a lawyer to say so,' and to be on the safe side he gave him six calendar months. Oh God no, Cedric, don't have any truck with lawyers." "I'll take your advice, Brendan, and," he added humbly, "I'm glad you're here, for you're a rock of sense." "Don't mention it," says I as the young policeman indicated the time was up.

'Well, in the court a fellow says to Cedric, "Please read what's on the card." Cedric took the square of cellophane-covered pasteboard from the clerk of the court and read without much interest what was written on it, then with a wink at the magistrate he restored the card to the clerk without comment. The magistrate looked over the rim of his spectacles and enquired of the clerk, "Is the defendant unable to speak?" "I don't really know, sir," and to Cedric he says, "Are you unable to speak?" "Yes," says his nibs, "that is I am able to speak." "Then why don't you read what's printed upon the card?" "But I have read it – and very good sentiments are those expressed too, sir." A little man in the body of the court gave a little snigger. "Any more displays like that," said the magistrate, "and I will clear the court. Now, I want you to read aloud what's on that card, young man." "Oh," said Cedric, "aloud." "Aloud," said the clerk of the court. "I swear by Almighty God that the evidence I give to this court shall be the truth, the whole truth, and nothing but the truth, so help me God." "So help you *who*?" asked the magistrate. "God," replied Cedric. "But," said the magistrate, "there is nothing like that on the card, is there?" "No, sir, but I decided it probably just got left out by mistake, I mean I'm a great filmgoer and in film courts there——" "Young man," said the judge, "kindly remember that this is one of Her Majesty's courts and not an American film studio. Please disregard all that the defendant has said after the words . . . and nothing but the truth." "Yes, sir," said the clerk, and to Cedric he said, "Is your name Cedric Joseph Toodle and do you live at 147 Queen Victoria Street, London NW11?" "It is, sir, and I do." "You are charged that on the morning of 19th December you did so behave in a public place, to wit Queen Victoria Street, in a manner likely to effect a breach of public order and discipline, do you plead guilty or not guilty?" "Guilty, sir, but, of course, it was only a joke. I mean to say, your honour, you know yourself how good it is sometimes to have a bit of a giggle." "You will confine yourself, young man, to pleading guilty or not guilty at this stage of the proceedings and at no time shall you presume to conclude how I would behave. What are the circumstances surrounding the charge?" "Please, sir," said Constable William Kieller, "on the morning of 19th December, while patrolling my beat at NW11 in company with Police Constable 1234 Nolan we were disturbed, shocked, and disgusted to perceive the defendant running towards us and brandishing a carving knife." The magistrate gave a "this is worthwhile quoting" look in the direction of the press box and said, "I can appreciate your being disturbed and shocked by the sight of a man brandishing a knife, but tell me, Constable, why should it disgust you?" "He was naked, sir." "Naked!" "He'd no clothes on, sir; in other words he was in his skin." "I am well aware, Constable, what constitutes the state of being naked." "Yes, sir." "Carry on, then." As the policeman proceeded to give a highly coloured account of what he thought occurred on the morning in question I whispered to Cedric's wife,

"Look at him, will you, for God's sake look at him grinning away there as though he were the chief feed in some comedy show. He'll get six months if he keeps this up, and as true as God I don't think I'd have much pity on him." Firna's face was a picture of puzzled anxiety: "I'll be glad when the whole dreadful business is over, Brendan, I'm sure everybody has the idea he's some sort of a half-wit. Why does he stand there like a spectator at a public meeting?" "Pride," said I, "stupid bloody pride. He just wants to show them all up as a crowd of conventional morons. Alright, so they are a bit state-bound and legal-minded, but he should remember that they have the whip hand at the moment, and it wouldn't cost that old judge a thought to give him six months."

'Police Constable Nolan then took the stand and corroborated the evidence given by his colleague. Then the magistrate turned to the still smiling Cedric and asked, "Have you anything to say?" "Nothing, sir, apart from the fact that I'd like you to know that I found the carry-on here this morning most interesting and well worth the trouble of a visit. I am, however, compelled to throw some cold water on the cosiness of the programme by pointing out to your two comrades," and here he indicated the two constables, "that they are mistaken in thinking that I ran along Victoria Street naked. I did no more than stand in my own garden and since it happens not to be a public place I find that the police have not established a *prima facie* case and therefore move that there is no charge for the jury to consider or the defendant to answer." "There is no jury sitting in this case," said the judge. "Well, not to worry, sir, they are about all that's needed to make this a real court. Anyway, since you are not wearing a wig I conclude that you are not yet fully qualified and I suppose they think you're not quite ready to have a jury of your own. However, take it from me you've done a grand job and they can't possibly keep you waiting much longer for your twelve good men and true. Now I must be going, where do I pay this five shillings, or is it twenty?"

'The magistrate's eyes bulged as he considered how best to temper his justice with mercy, but his temper got the better of him and he all but shouted, "There will be no fine in this case." "Oh good man," said Cedric. "Thank you, sir." As he made to leave the court the judge said, "For the next two weeks I shall ensure that you are suitably clad in prison garb at all hours of the day. I find the case proven and sentence you to fourteen days." Cedric clung to the dock and his body swayed. "Fourteen days?" he asked. "Fourteen days," said the judge. "Fourteen days," said I; "begod, Firna, but he has the luck of the devil!" "Oh, Brendan," said she, "take me home." "God help yeh," says I, "of course I will." Yeh know, Gainor, but I've seldom spent a better fortnight!' 'And that was a cousin of yours?' Gainor asked Podmore. 'He was,' grinned the latter. 'But that's nothing to him, is it, Podmore? Sure that fella shows everybody he meets a picture of his mother – NAKED.' The Ginger Man raised his eyebrows. I went back to work.

9

'Come into the garden Maud
For the black bat night has flown
Come into the garden Maud
I'm here at the gate alone.'

WE WERE PAINTING A HOTEL in Youghal, Co. Cork, when, looking out of a window, Brendan said to me, 'Yeh know, when the sun takes a grip of the top of the sea out there, and throws up a warm haze, an' yeh start thinkin' of the history of a place like this, yeh realise that to write is the *only* thing. Just imagine it now. Not thirty miles from where we're standin', Tom Barry's flyin' column set about the Black and Tans and frightened the bloody shite out of them. "Burn Cork, will yeh," said the bould Tom, "I'll give yeh crematin' if that's what yer wantin'." An' by jazes, every last one of them got it. Then there was McSweeny from the same place, Lord Mayor of Cork, and the man to stick the longest hunger strike in history. Killed him, of course. And the chaps in the Curragh wantin' us to do the same caper. Didn't understand tactics, yeh see. Lenin now; ah, there was a man for the political moment. What was right yesterday can easily be wrong tomorrow. McSweeny's hunger strike was a victory-death and all. It engaged the attention of the world. But then think of Tony Darcy and Jack McNeela; Lenin could have told them that De Valera would let them die. The world didn't care. We weren't fightin' the British Empire, we were fightin' ourselves. We were fightin' a civil war. There's a great novel in that very same battle. Could be like *War and Peace*. Ah, but it was alright for Tolstoy, he didn't have to run around cleanin' up every house that had a load of bugs and not enough do-it-yourself to get rid of them. Painting kips and grander kips! There's an existence for men that should be out writing! What in the namea jazes are we doin' wastin' our youth here?' I knew he was including me with himself because I was – in name, anyway – with Rory, his boss. 'D'ye ever re-write?' he asked. J shook my head. 'Yeh should. Yeh should,' he replied. 'I've been reading your *Songs of a Dublin Rebel* and they're good, mind yeh – God, I was nearly goin' to say promising ... what a stupid bloody word that is to connect with talent. A real publisher's word, or, worse than that, a critic's. But yeh should re-write. And get it typed.' He paused for a moment to pick his nose and asked, 'Is the other fella below?' 'Rory's gone out with Peter for a while,' I answered. 'Then,' said he, 'I'll have time to slip over to the *Green Park* for a curer.' 'I'm sorry, Brendan, but Rory and Peter said you have to get this room finished today.' He put down his brush, scowled, and shook his fist in my face. 'Yeh skinny bastard!' he roared, 'yer no better than a screw! Nobody but the meanest nark in the world would deny a dyin' man a drink!' And, as I went out of the room, I could hear him add to the closing door, 'Write! Yeh couldn't write yer fuckin' name on a time sheet!'

I went back to my own task of painting a crown ceiling which covered the well of a staircase sixty feet high, and I hadn't done much before I heard a familiar voice whispering, 'That's rather dangerous, isn't it, Brendan?' 'It is, Podmore,' Brendan returned, 'and I'd nearly pray to Christ that he'd fall and break his bloody neck but I'd never hear the end of it from my mother.' 'Hello, Dominic,' Podmore greeted me as I noticed his presence. 'Where the hell did you spring out of?' I asked. 'From a bloody big Mercedes,' said Brendan, 'that's goin' to take he and I to a party.' 'At four o'clock in the afternoon?' I asked. 'Four or five in the mornin' or evenin', what's the bloody difference? There's hardly a special time for drinkin',' said my brother. 'But,' I asked, 'a party?' He grinned and did his favourite little dance accompanied by his singing of the children's street song: 'Yer all too dirty, dirty, dirty, yer all too dirty I'll tell you.' Then, breaking off in the middle, he said, 'It's a garden party.' 'A garden party,' I said. 'A garden party. Yeh may remember I had a play on Radio Eireann with the name.' 'I remember, and not very good if I remember rightly,' I replied, still smarting under his sneer at my literary pretensions. 'Well,' he said, 'it was a damn' sight more good than anything you've ever done. Thirty guineas more good.' 'I didn't know you wrote?' asked Podmore. 'Oh yes,' interrupted Brendan, 'he's a well-known poet of the cause, writes "Up the Republic" on lavatory walls.' 'Maybe you'd care to join us, Dominic?' Podmore asked. 'Not if I'm bloody conscious,' snarled Brendan. I hadn't had any intention of leaving the job, but now, because I realised my presence would annoy him, I said, 'Delighted,' and in a flash I was down from the scaffolding, washed my hands in turps, and threw off my overalls.

I can't remember the name of the Lord at whose home the garden party was to be held, but I know he was one of Podmore's uncles and his place was some twenty miles from where we were working. 'Is this a dress affair?' I asked. Brendan stopped abusing the countryside and its inhabitants, and said, 'Jazes but yer as thick as shite. Who ever heard of a dressed garden party?' 'Well,' I said, 'they might have morning dress.' 'Well, they don't, and that's an end to that. If yeh want to make conversation talk about somethin' worth while. "Is this a dress affair?" ' Brendan mimicked, 'what would yeh know about it even if it was?' 'Well,' I said, 'I've been at two dress dances which is twice as many as yerself.' ' 'Tis not if yeh want to know. I was rigged out twice by Jimmy Bourke; once as the devil, and then as Saint Patrick. Christ! that was a laugh. There I was walkin' over O'Connell Bridge in me bishop's rig-out, and didn't a poor oulwan take me for a real bishop and I, beginnin' to believe in me own episcopal authority, ordered her and a crowd of others to kneel down for me blessin'. I was workin' for "Early", the church decorators, at the time, and I had one of the hands off a statue in under the sleeve of me robe. Well, be the laughin' jazes, I blessed the oulwan first, then, as she stooped to kiss me ring, I left the tiny little hand in her own and, God love her! she nearly died of fright. While this poor thing was starin' at her hand in horror I suddenly got sick and spewed over the rest of them. Begod, but Jesse Owens couldn't have held a candle to me that evenin' as I broke all sprint records up O'Connell Street.'

Briefly, the garden party appealed to Brendan until he had drunk a certain amount, after which he decided that the public should be suitably shocked. There were murmurs here and there about his 'tongue' and I suppose he had really taken as much as he was able for one day when, almost without warning, he started to march around a group of tweedy people singing as he went: 'Some Girls Marry for Love'. This bit of his repertoire 'sorted out the lady women from the *ladies'*, he maintained – the latter being the only ones bad minded enough to see in the words of the song a dirty double meaning:

'Now some girls marry for love
And more girls marry for riches,

But gimme the girl who marries the man
For what he has in his bringing
The children off to school
And beating them with a stick,
Before they've learned their A.B.C.
They're fiddling with their Mick
McGilligan had a dog and
A very good dog was he,
He gave it to a lady friend
To keep her company
The dog ran in and the dog ran out
And we all went on the hunt
But where d'ye think the little dog went
But up the lady's country girls are
Very fine girls for rolling in the
Grass, take out your old thermometer
And shove it up her artificial
Musical boxes work when you them wind,
And if you think my song is bad
The dirt is in your mind.'

At the end of which he proceeded to walk in and out of the guests with staggering stride, pretending to blow a bugle, and going:

'Ta rah de dah, yer only jokin'
Tar rah de dah, yer pulling me leg,
Ta rah de dah, yer only jokin'
Yer pullin' yer pullin' yer pullin'
Yer pullin' me leg yer pullin' me leg.'

The host, instead of ringing for the police, as I feared he might, merely asked his guests to forgive the performance, and suggested that it might be as well 'if Mr Behan left as

Mr Behan appeared to be a little tired'. Later I listened as Brendan retold the story of the garden party and how he came to be ejected because of his dislike for the pretence of the pretentious Irish upper class.

'Well, jazes,' he told the customers of the Dawson Lounge, 'yeh never saw the likes – did they, Dominic.' 'They didn't, Brendan,' I confirmed. 'Did they, Podmore?' he demanded of Osbert. Podmore agreed too.

'There's one thing I can't bloody well stand. And that's me own people actin' as though they must bow so low for the Angst that they have to nearly bloody well dig a hole to get down low enough. And they'd a bloody waiter there like that; hadn't they, Podmore?' The latter agreed.

'But I took the while-coated gett back to earth. Didn't I, Dominic?'

'Yeh did, Brendan.'

'There was as much brandy there for the takin',' Brendan went on, 'and I said to this waiter, "I'd like a brandy please – a large one." "Certainly sir." Down I threw it, gulped another couple, and said, "Try one yerself, mac." He smiled a waiter's professional waiter smile and said, "Not while I'm on duty, sir." "But it's free – gratis; for nothin' like." "Not while I'm on duty, sir." Like a bloody slave parrot. "Do you not drink?" "I beg your pardon, sir?" "My pardon," said I, "is not worth begging." "Just an expression, sir." "Yes, like a good many more handed down by people who never stopped to think."

'Then this other eejit here,' and Brendan indicated me, 'he says, "Brendan, they have Guinness here too." "Well damn you, sir," I replied, "how dare you suggest that my proper place is behind a Guinness bottle!" "But," said he, "I was just thinkin' . . ." "Well," I said, "stop at once; the unfamiliar exercise will do your brain an injury!" ' I remembered trying to prevent Brendan drinking too much brandy without much success. And strangely enough I could also see that there was a general truth about Brendan's account of everything – and much more entertaining.

'Of course, then,' said Brendan, 'we had to join the enemy at some time. And jazes, when we did. Yeh never in yer life come across such an overdressed, over-accented, over-Piccadilly-looking lot in your natural. Podmore here made the introductions and with a lot of touching of finger-ends and "delighted I'm sures" to their "delighted I'm sures" – did yeh ever notice about that class of people? They never shake hands. Even when they dance it seems as if the women might be ready to break.

'One fella kneels admiring a bed of blooms and is so langers drunk that when he tries to get up he nearly falls over. So I took me bould Podmore away and promised to act them all, and didn't I, Podmore?' 'You did, Brendan,' Podmore affirmed.

'Did yeh ever see Toulouse Lautrec?' Brendan asked. 'He was so small that when he was charged one time with something or other and didn't appear to appear the judge issued a warrant for his arrest. Poor old Toolie couldn't be seen behind the dock.' Brendan took his shoes off; knelt in them and proceeded to scud around the bar on his knees, raging as he went about art being the province of tall men.

'Of course that's nothing compared to our horsy friends, "And poor Emily was found in a kitchen with her head inside a gas stove and all the taps turned on. Oh what a dreadful accident! Doors and windows sealed. Coroner returns verdict, balance of mind disturbed. Could have happened to anybody."

' "And yourself, Colonel. Told to leave India by the natives." "Gone to the dogs. Like Ireland, you know. Oh.

that's where the rot set in." "There myself in '36 when they tried to blow up the Queen." "The Queen?" "Yes, Queen Victoria, in stone on Leinster Lawn." "How awful!" "And Gough in the Phoenix Park lost a leg – or was it his horse?" "Goodness of the gracious! Nelson alright I hope?" "Planning to put Kevin Barry up there." "Kevin Barry alongside Nelson? Never!" "I think they mean instead of Nelson." "Oh dear dear!" "And Victoria is now in a rubbish dump – a Ballsbridge one. Upper class, you know." "But, sir, dammitall a rubbish dump is a rubbish dump." "Working people prefer working class ones, I believe." Of course in the middle of my acting these vulgarians, the chief one says to Podmore, "Your friend is no longer welcome. Please ask him to leave." Didn't he, Podmore?' Podmore agreed and Brendan continued, 'But I looked around me for a minit and asked, "Why is this poor eejit talkin' to me like somethin' out of one of me uncle's melodramas? Is it me larinix, mister? Oh, I'm sorry, 'larynx'. Would yeh ever take five shillin's and have a mass said for yerself?" "You are a cad, sir." "I am that. But tell me, are yeh takin' anything for yer own complaint?" "Oh, I was never more . . ." "And, sir, I hope you'll never be less." "How dare you!" "I dare very well. How dare you? With your mouth full of hot potatoes. How distressing it must be to meet with an ad cantus leper. I am to bow my head whenever some horsy bastard softens a vowel or hardens a consonant – and usually in the wrong place."

' "Well, some *people*," this oul geeser says. "Yes," says I, "but I *am* a person. You lot are not here at all! You don't exist. With your livin' in humes and silvery dumes. You're not human; you're pictures of people!"

'Then I told him how I had taught one of Podmore's relations to speak English. D'ye remember that fellow, Podmore, the Estonian prince that married yer cousin?'

Podmore did remember. 'His mother,' Brendan went on, 'thought that it would be a good idea if I was to take what-ye-may-call-him around with me to learn the language.' 'Dimitry,' supplied Podmore. 'Aye,' remembered Brendan, 'Dimitry. I suppose I must have been the most unusual English tutor ever made since the Holy Ghost spoke in divers tongues the wonderful works of God. Yeh know, for years I thought that the Shadow – as we called old Holy – used to be referring to a language spoken by deep sea divers.

'After hawking this Dimitry fella around some of the lowest pubs in Dublin he finally thought he had graduated from my peculiar academy of languages. And there they are seated round a table at Podmore's family seat. Nuns, priests, bishops, archbishops, and even bloody cardinals – if me information is correct. And Dimitry is called upon by Podmore's mother, "Dimitry! Is it time for cocktails?" And serious Dimitry, taking his first steps into the angle worlds without me, and with a look at his watch, replies gravely in sonorous tones, "Eet ees tenn to focking saven." '

10

'Thunder and lightning it's no lark
When Dublin city is in the dark
If you have any money go up to the park
And view the Zoological gardens.'

'OH, BRENDAN,' SAID MY AUNT Maggie Trimble, 'what sort of a place is this?' 'Put yer mind at rest, Maggie,' said Brendan, 'it's one of the most noted houses in the city. What would yeh like now?' Maggie sat back on a seat with three legs over a hole, Brendan's right knee placed under the seat top made the fourth leg to keep Maggie upright. 'I'd love a little drop of sweet sherry, Brendan.' 'Tom,' Brendan cried to the barman, 'bring us two glasses of the red!' Tom looked sharply at my brother and demanded, 'Are yeh a cripple or what that yeh can't get up and get it?' 'No,' replied Brendan, 'but if I take my knee from under this seat me Aunt Maggie is goin' to fall into a hole.' Over at the fireplace a man stood in front of the roaring coals and Aunt Maggie saw steam rising above him. 'Oh Lord God, Brendan, that man is doin' his water into the fire.' 'Aye, Maggie, the oul lavatory is choked up.' 'God preserve us,' said my aunt, 'but I thought yeh said this was a respectable place.' 'No, Maggie, I said noted. There yeh are, Tom,' he said, as the barman approached with two pint glasses of redness. 'Merciful hour,' said Maggie, 'I asked for wine.' 'And wine yer gettin',' replied Brendan, 'and it's the best of the stock. Made here on the premises and none of yer imported rubbish. Pay the man, Maggie, he's waitin'.' My aunt opened her purse and extracted a ten-shilling note. Brendan, peering down, said, 'Yeh've smaller than that there, Maggie.' 'Only a shillin', Brendan.' 'Well, give that to him and we'll have another two pints on the change.' Tom said apologetically, 'I'm sorry, Brendan, but it's up a penny. That'll be another fourpence please, mam.' Maggie handed him the four extra pence and he thanked her regally. 'Lord, Brendan,' she complained, 'but I'd sooner have a small drop of the foreign stuff, I think.' 'God forgive yeh, Maggie Trimble, and in the middle of a great campaign to buy Irish. Were yeh ever in France?' 'Indeed, Brendan, I was never in me life out of Ireland than to bury poor Mollie's husband in County Meath.' 'Well, then, if yeh could have seen them as I did standin' on the grapes and crushin' them with their feet.' 'Yer jokin', Brendan Behan! And not with their boots on?' 'In their bare feet, Mag.' 'Well, may the Lord look sideways on me if I ever touch another drop of foreign spirit.'

Two whores started to fight and began to tear each other by the hair. Then they took off their shoes to use them as weapons and struck at the windows and mirrors, but everything breakable was protected by stout wire grilles and their efforts were of no avail. 'Brendan,' said Tom, who busily scratched his head and stood with arms folded behind the bar, 'lock that door and don't let them on to the street – they'll make a show of the place.' 'Oh Lord God,' said Maggie, 'that fella that was waterin' the fire is comin' over to us. And his dress is not adjusted.' 'Ah sure, he's alright, Maggie, a decent sort. Eh, Tombo,' he cried, 'before yeh come into decent company bend down till I whisper somethin' into yer ear.' Tombo inclined his head and Brendan nearly burst the man's eardrums with a roar of, 'Close yer bloody fly, yeh silly bastard!' Brendan exploded with laughter and said, 'See that fella, Maggie? Well, it's him that I call Crippen in the *Irish Press*.' 'I'll never read it again, Brendan. To think of a fella like that findin' his way into a person's newspaper. It's positively indecent. Oh, Brendan Behan, this is a quare place, there's them two that was fightin' a minit ago with their arms around each other like friends.' 'Ah,' said Brendan, 'all is forgiven.' 'Dear God! They must be very low. Only tinker women fight and make up.'

A plump jolly woman entered and she was wearing an apron with wide linen pockets from which came the comforting jingle of many coins. Seeing Brendan in the corner she cried, 'Well, there yeh are as large as life, Brendan! God, yer gettin' as fat as a fool! Will yeh have somethin'?' 'Thanks, Mary, but I'm here with me aunt in company.' One of the whores said quite audibly, 'A likely story, but don't think that she's comin' to take the bread out of our mouths. Jazes, yeh ought to have more sense, Brendan Behan. Sure that oul wan is well past her labour.' Tom leaned over and grabbed her by the shoulder and said, 'Show a bit of good manners and courtesy to that lady or I'll put me fist through yer face.' The whore wrenched herself free, stood back, and taunted, 'Will yeh now? You and what army? Look at him, girls, will yeh, for jazes' sake look at Samson. When he was in the army they didn't know if he was the biggest dwarf or the smallest giant in the regiment.' 'I'll send for the polis,' said Tom. 'Don't be boastin',' said the whore, 'no self-respectin' polisman would be caught dead in this kip.' 'Don't mind that one, mam,' said Mary, as she sat beside Aunt Maggie, 'she's as vulgar as cowshite. Wipe her arse for her and all yeh'd get would be abuse. Of course then, what can yeh expect from a pig but a grunt. Get up there, Brendan, and tell the man we want a drink. And none of that bloody paraffin oil either, mind yeh. Lord, mam,' she said to Maggie, 'I'm surprised at yerself drinkin' the likes of that.' 'Diamond eyes here,' said Maggie, pointing to Brendan, 'told me it was the very best.' 'I did not,' replied Brendan, 'I said it was Irish.' 'So was the famine,' said Mary, 'but who wants a glass of that? Get up there and get three whiskeys and three bottles of stout, Brendan.' 'I'll call the waiter,' said Brendan. 'Oh,' said Mary, 'call the waiter how are yeh. We're very grand today. Of course it's gettin' yer name in the papers does that. Jazes, I'll never forget my fella and him writin' to the *Evenin' Mail* tellin' them that every good Irishman should stand by Parnell.' 'Sure your husband couldn't have been around during Parnell's time,' said Brendan. 'Of course not, but my Billser was only sober once durin' his whole life and the only time he'd ever heard tell of the man was last year when someone was talkin' about it in hospital when he was takin' the cure. "Billser," says I, "do yeh not know that Parnell is dead?" "I'm not surprised," says he, "sure the whole carry-on was enough to kill anyone." ' Maggie sat not knowing what to do or say in what she decided was low company, but as Brendan ordered the drink he gave her a reassuring wink and she smiled politely to Mary and enquired, 'And what does your husband do, mam, if it's not too personal a question?' 'He's dead, mam.' 'Oh, I'm sorry to hear that, the Lord rest his soul.' 'Well, he was the greatest little bastard, missus, the Lord be good to him and grant him eternal comfort. Never from the day and hour I married him did that little gett ever move his arse outa joint unless it was to get to the pub before closin' time.' Brendan laughed loudly and asked, 'And what did yeh see in him, Mary?' Her laughter lines creased all together and with a twinkle in her eye she said, 'Well, Brendan, yeh know the ould sayin', little jockeys have big whips. Though when I think of him as I saw him first in the uniform of the

Dublin Fusiliers he was a handsome little fella. Lord, I was often wonderin', if the Germans had seen the British Army stripped would they have given up so easily? A uniform, like a petticoat, hides a hell of a lot. And was your husband in the army, mam?' she asked my aunt. 'He was in the Post Office,' said Maggie, with a proud shake of the head. 'Oh,' Mary beamed, 'wasn't he the sensible man, instead of gettin' himself killed in Flanders or someplace, he found a nice steady job. Yeh must be very comfortably off, if yeh don't mind my sayin' so.' Brendan intervened to say, 'He was fightin' for the Republic, Mary, in 1916.' 'Oh,' said Mary, 'is it *that* Post Office? Well, God, more power to him, sure every cripple has his own way of walkin'. My fella might have done the same had he been here. But sure I suppose he'd have had to fight for the countrymen as well and that would never have suited him. Always said that they were comin' outa the bog to take the work from him.' 'I thought,' said Brendan, 'he never did any work?' 'Neither he did, son. But he didn't like to see them take it away from the fellas he knew. Gave him great satisfaction to watch men diggin' a hole in the road while he was waitin' for the pubs to open.' A small neatly dressed man passed in the direction of the lavatory and Mary whispered, 'Pay no attention to that fella. An interferin' faggot. Yeh know who he is, don't yeh, Brendan?' 'I don't then,' replied the latter. 'Sure that's the brother of the fella yeh met last Saturday in Floods. God, mam,' she turned to Maggie laughing, 'we were havin' a few jars and mindin' our own business when this thing comes over with a copy of the *Irish Press* and Brendan's weekly article in it. He's a schoolteacher, yeh see, and thinks nobody else in the world knows about things but himself. Well, I've always said if Brendan Behan is a bit of a show in the oul rags he wears, and mind yeh I mean it, Brendan, yeh ought to have more respect for the people yeh come from then be goin' around them hoity toity pubs like a man on leave from a tip head. Anyway, yer one of our own, and as I say meself if yeh didn't go to school yeh met the scholars on the way home. This gobshite comes up to him and real imperint like says to Brendan, "I didn't like your story in this mornin's paper." Ah but jazes them fellas shouldn't pick on the likes of us if it's fight they're wantin', as quick as a flash me bould son here turned on him and says, "How much did yeh pay for that paper?" "The usual price," says the other fella. "Well, then," says Brendan, "there's yer money now, F off outa this, d'ye think that yeh can speak to decent people for the sake of a threepenny bit?" An' jazes, mam, I threw him another six-pence for his bus fare.' 'And not a haporth of bother to yeh, mam,' said Maggie, who immediately warmed to anybody defending her nephew. 'Oh, mam, would I allow it? Some oul thick that doesn't know his arse from his elbow, wantin' to make little of a man that writes for a paper. And I hear yer goin' to act in a play as well, Lord Almighty but ye've got brains to burn.' 'I'm not actin' in it, Mary,' said Brendan, 'I've written it and it's bein' produced at the Pike Theatre.' 'Yeh wrote it? The whole lot of it, yeh mean? All by yerself? What's it about?' 'Hanging,' said Brendan. Mary smiled grimly in approval. 'And about time too. Yeh know there's a shower of bastards live around my sister's place in Kimmage and I'd love someone to take a rope to the lot of them. Of course, there'll be objections. Like there was to Chamberpot.' 'Chamberpot?' asked Brendan. 'Yes, that's what my fella used to call him. The head of the English government that was. My fella could never remember things for a minit and everybody would be laughin' their heads off at him as he spoke seriously about Mr Chamber-pot talkin' to Hitler and my fella wouldn't know a haporth about it. Oh a proper gobshite. But, sure, so was all before him. If it was rainin' soup they'd be out there with forks. Drink up there, Brendan, and sing us a song.' 'Sing one yerself, Mary,' suggested the latter. 'I will begod, as I said to the priest on the mornin' of me weddin'.'

Mary was halfway through *A Rose in a Garden of Weeds* when Brendan rose to go to the lavatory and the two women fell into the hole. 'Well, the cursea God on yeh, Brendan Behan!' she cried, 'but if yeh didn't want me to sing yeh'd a right to ask me to stop. Well,' she shouted, 'will yeh stop yer chucklin' and lift me out of this. Begod, I've heard of a body being in a hole.' 'Brendan Behan,' said Maggie, 'I've had as much as a body can put up with. Now take me out of this terrible place this very minit.' Brendan grinned and said, 'We'll go now, Mag, I have me story for tomorra's paper. Good luck, Mary, and God bless yeh.' 'God bless yerself, Brendan, and may yeh never take a spoonful of bad money.' Brendan and Maggie had already opened the door when Mary called, 'Brendan, I was nearly forgetting, have yeh yer fare now, son?' 'I have, Mary,' he replied. 'Musha God love yeh,' she called.

11

'I've polished me pewter, I've tidied me kitchen
Me dresser is white as a stack in the snow
   And while at me window me skirt I've been stitchin'
For I'm very neat with the needle to sew
   Says I "what's the use of me mendin' me finery
Till it's all fit for a queen on her throne
   Och sure there isn't the sign of me
Gettin' a man and a house of me own"
   Haste to the weddin', oh, haste to the weddin'
I sing as I sit by me window alone
   Ah sure it's oft' I've been frettin'
I'll not get a man and a house of me own.'

'I LIKED YER ARTICLE in this mornin's paper, Brendan.' His retort would depend on why it was said. 'Thank yeh very much, and God bless yeh,' he would reply to the well-meaning. To the 'knockers', as he called them, he would exclaim, 'Don't for the love of jazes either like or dislike them.' He maintained that there were people anxiously waiting round the pubs of Grafton Street with a wedge dipped in praise and soaked in procrastination. Other writers think this way too. I was in Neary's of Chatham Street shortly after my book *Teems of Times and Happy Returns* was published. I had just interviewed J. P. Donleavy, author of *The Ginger Man*, and we were having a drink at the bar when a man sidled up and said to me, 'I've just read your book.' Before I could acknowledge the comment, Donleavy picked an empty cigarette carton from a tray on the counter and, having written something upon it, folded the packet and silently indicated that I should offer it to the stranger. I did so, and with an astonished stare at the message the man left. 'Next move was your automatic reply, "How did you like it?" And he delightedly drags from his mind a vindictive, "Diabolical!" They wait,' said Donleavy, 'for the unwary and make your life a misery. You are aware that their only aim is to annoy, and yet nobody looks for condemnation.'

Brendan neither liked nor disliked what he wrote for the *Irish Press*. He defended the paper because it had 'less dead priests' than it's opposite number, the *Independent*. 'Yeh can't read the racin' part of that rag but a deceased monsignor or an ailing cardinal gets himself between the horses and the jockeys.' Neither did he let anybody forget that the *Independent* called for the execution of James Connolly, one of the leaders of the 1916 Rising.

Brendan in the paper was a person with whom the mass of Irish people could identify themselves. Like the Beatles or Eamonn Andrews, he was one of their own. They laughed to see their idiomatic peculiarities in print, and then, realising that they had as much right to be as idiosyncratic as the next group, took pleasure in the reading. 'I told him a story about me fella,' said a Kimmage woman to me, 'and there it was starin' me in the face. Starin' at me out of the paper. And I hid it under the sofa, and me fella comes tearin' the house an' says to me, and me terrified outa me wits that he'd find it, "Julia, will yeh get me the *Press* till I read yeh the funniest thing yeh've ever see in yer life." It's about me, be Brendan. Though God love him I've a mind to thump him for the laughin' stock he's made of me. God! isn't he the gas man!"'

John Ryan published Brendan in his magazine *Envoy*. Peader O'Donnell in the *Bell*. He was drama critic for a late-night programme on Radio Eireann until shortly after his appointment he reviewed a pre-West End production of *Hippo Dancers*. He said, 'It's impact was like the banging together of two damp dishcloths.' Nobody was quite ready for the man who described John Osborne as 'being as angry as Mrs Dale's diary'.

When his friend Patrick Kavanagh, the Irish poet, sued the *Leader* for libel, Brendan's name became even more known in Ireland. So well known that a lot of people didn't want to know him at all. He was I suppose more notorious than famous. Kavanagh was questioned as to his friendship with Brendan and said, 'I don't know the man.' He was at least offensive, according to what Kavanagh said about him in court. Then the defence received a copy of Kavanagh's book *Tarry Flynn*, inscribed to Brendan.

People were under the impression that Brendan had handed the book in just as earlier they had believed him to be the author of the article in which Kavanagh was libelled. The piece on Kavanagh was not written by Brendan and the book was handed into court by my brother Rory. Big brother would thump the nation in defence of his Benjamin.

Brendan, hurt that anybody should even think him capable of such an act, refused to confirm or deny the allegations being made and insinuated about his connection with the case. I didn't see Kavanagh in Brendan's company since before the case they each had a bowl of my mother's soup. I remember that occasion because Kavanagh pleased her so much when he described the broth as being 'a meal of Elizabethan proportions'.

People who know of Brendan think his silence over the Kavanagh affair uncharacteristic of him, to say the least. They have been blinded by the legend. Like his granny, he was secretive and silent, which is rather strange for two people born and brought up in Dublin.

'Country people are as talkative as the tomb,' was a favourite jibe of his. In *Brendan Behan's Island* he writes of a murder in Kerry. The police could elicit no information regarding the murder from anybody around. Then one member of the Garda, questioning a reluctant old woman, asked in exasperation, 'Tell me, mam, do you know anything?' And he pointed out over the Atlantic Ocean to the Blasket Islands lying out in the bay and he said, 'Tell me, mam,' he says, 'do you know the names of those three islands out there?' 'I couldn't tell you, sir,' she said, 'they weren't here when I'd gone to bed last night.'

My wife Josephine, or, as my mother calls her, Siobhan, told me of the first time she discussed Brendan with my mother. It must have been at most about two minutes after they both had met because his name is never far from Ma's conversation.

'I was walkin' down the road, Siobhan,' began Ma, 'with me old market bag in me arms, and a huge big car drove up beside me. It nearly came up on the pavement! and the door opened and out jumped Brendan. Says he to me, "Jump in, Mother!" and off we went.

'We went to this pub, Kenneddy's of Harold's Cross Bridge – upstairs. And there was a fire there. And there was two little girls with Brendan, and they had buttons on – flowers like. So, of course, I jumped up and lifted me skirts and started to sing "Haste to the Weddin'". Oh! we had a grand time! And I, of course, had to leave because I had to get home to cook the tea for Da and Dom.

'And Dominic came in – I couldn't wait to tell him. And

I says to Dominic, "Dom, I've had the best of a time with Brendan." And I started to tell him about the jollity and about me liftin' me skirts and singin' "Haste to the Weddin'." And Dominic says, "Mother, d'ye not know that yeh were singin' at Brendan's weddin'?" And I says, "Darlin', no!" And he says, "But yeh were. He was married this mornin'."

'Well, around seven o'clock there was a knock on the door, and this big huge car was waitin' outside the garden wall, and Brendan, "Mother," he says, "where's me two shirts? I've got to go to France." I had them by the fireside airing.

'I says to him, "Brendan, is it true yer married?" And he turns to poor Dom in the corner and said, "Did that skinny little f. tell yeh?" So he grabs a hold of the shirts and I said to him, "Is it true? Are yeh married?" And with tears runnin' down his cheeks he grabs me in his arms and says, "Mother, don't yeh know I'll never love anyone the way I love you?"

'And off he ran out – he didn't even parcel the shirts, just hands them in to Beatrice sittin' waitin' in the car that her father, Cecil, was drivin'. Off they went, and I thought about his poor old socks – yeh know, I hadn't enough wool, Siobhan, to finish them, so I made the toes orange. And says I to meself, "Now what on earth will that poor girl think of me?" I wonder why he did that, Siobhan? Get married and not tell me. Sure don't they know I just love to see young people happy?'

When he came back from France and met my mother shortly after his return she told him I was planning to be married and that I would like him to act as best man. She had begged me to wed in a church and I had refused. When Brendan heard that the wedding was to be a civil ceremony he refused to have anything to do with it: 'I'll see you in hell first!' he shouted. Being doubtful about that, I set about the business of organising another witness.

On the eve of the wedding he came to see me at Kimmage. 'No one will be best man at this affair but me. I've made the arrangements for the reception, or should I say receptions, there'll be one in my place in the mornin' for the layabouts who don't work, and one here in the evenin' for the poor bastards who have to.'

When he had finished telling me how he had put the wedding banns into the *Irish Times*, the only paper he knew to be not widely taken among the working class, he added his stroke of genius, 'I wrote them in Irish because the other classes don't know any.' I told him that I'd like him to come for a drink with Josephine and I. He rounded on me, as they say. 'Have yeh no idea of tradition? The slightest respect for people's customs? I can understand, maybe, that yeh won't abide by a tradition which forces yeh into a chapel against yer agnostic principles. But surely yeh'll accept an old-fashioned custom like not seeing yer future wife the night before yer married?' I said I didn't know anything about it. He just shook his head at me and warned, 'Close friends, mind yeh! No one else! I haven't got respect for much meself, but I'm damned if I'd like the world to know me brother was married in a solicitor's anteroom!' Then as he got to the hall door he asked Josephine, 'Tell me, child – you as should know – is he really such a gobshite?'

I went to meet my wife at the register office on the following morning and was greeted by a chalked legend, 'Gone to Bowes pub. with J. Wait. B.' 'Never saw anything like it, Dom,' said my wife. 'There he was with no way to tell you where we had gone. And he stops a couple of kids in the street and says, "Excuse me, lads, but will one of yeh give me a bit of chalk." I thought it was a daft idea. But, sure enough, one of the children puts his hand down into the bottom of his bulging lining and up with an assortment of twine, marbles, nuts, and bolts, and what have, comes a piece of chalk.

'Then he pretends to be a paralytic and gets the sympathy of all the old women from here to the pub. And jumps up to get a tie in that shop "Menswear". Inside were about four young assistants. Brendan went up to one and demanded, "Where's Mr Menswear?" The young man tried to explain that there was no such person. "It's a trade name, sir."

' "Well, he'll do no more trade with me, I'm fed up gettin' left-hand hats when I need right-hand ones. If Mr Menswear is afraid to face me now I'll take a tie." And the young-fella asks him what sort of a tie he wants, and he looks at his waist and says, "About forty-six, I seem to be gettin' somewhat stout." Then he takes off his jacket to put the tie round his neck and everybody in the shop goggles at him. Paid the chap and then slouches out of the shop like Groucho Marx through the door and says, "Do you swear no but yer boss believes yeh do that's why he has that name on the shop men swear. Stop giggling, damn you. One tie four shillings, four assistants fifteen minutes, how can the country prosper when you people giggle over such a state of affairs?" '

'If you're not serious,' said the lawyer, 'I won't marry you at all.' 'Nobody's asking you,' said Brendan, 'he brought a perfectly good girl of his own.' 'If you don't stop making a joke of the ceremony I'll close the office.' And I begged Brendan to take it easy as the man was getting annoyed, 'Yes,' Brendan whispered, 'civil ceremonies are probably against his religion.' Then when we were married my brother took the astonished celebrant in his arms, pretended to kiss him, and cried, 'I hope you'll be very happy.'

Wedding or no wedding, Saturday was a working day, so

Da rolled home late in the evening to the second reception going full blast. He took a glass of whiskey and said, 'I like that. Young people enjoying themselves. Very nice.' 'Yeh seem to forget I was married this morning,' I told him. 'And,' he said, 'a sensible way to spend any Saturday. I lost every penny I had backin' horses.' 'I was in London last week talkin' to a friend of yours,' said Brendan in a whisper of rare confidence, 'Joan Littlewood, she's goin' to do *The Quare Fella*.' With a voice like a bell he started to sing and the room quietened, as he often said himself when somebody in the singing pubs asked, 'Order for the singer, ladies and gentlemen!' 'a good singer makes his own bloody order';

'A sober black shawl hides her body entirely,
Touched by the Sun and the salt spray of the sea,
But down in the darkness a slim hand so lovely,
Carries a rich bunch of red roses for me.'

I remembered when he had sung it as his curtain speech to the first night of *The Quare Fella* at the Pike and, as he finished, the applause from the audience in the little theatre to praise Alan Simpson and Carolyn Swift's guts for putting it on. The same Simpson who went handcuffed to jail in censorless Ireland because he put on a play which tended to 'deprave and corrupt': *The Rose Tattoo*.

We waited for the morning papers and I cursed the football critics of Ireland who wouldn't recognise the importance of *The Quare Fella* as the greatest dramatic play since O'Casey and his was flung out by the bell, book, and candleers. One Irish paper called it a '. . . stringing together of music-hall sketches'.

Joan Littlewood's production of *The Quare Fella* in May 1956 was well received. The critics were unanimous in their praise and I thought that Brendan had at last reached wherever it was he was going. Kenneth Tynan, a real critic, said, 'If the English hoard words like misers, the Irish spend them like sailors; and Brendan Behan, Dublin's obstreperous poet-playwright, is one of the biggest spenders in this line since the young Sean O'Casey. Behan sends language out on a swaggering spree, ribald, flushed, and spoiling for a fight.' And I thought to myself, 'That'll annoy some of the bastards around me, anyway.'

Nothing if not adventurous, the Abbey Theatre decided to try out *The Quare Fella*. Success at the Pike, at Stratford E.15, and at the Comedy might have been accepted as recommendation enough for any ordinary theatre. But this was the Abbey. First theatre to recognise Synge and O'Casey. Mr Behan's play would, of course, be considered in the ordinary way. Mr Blythe, the Abbey director, suggested that the play be seen by his producer, Miss Ria Mooney. My cousin Jimmy (he writes under the name Seamus de Burca) told me of Brendan's reply: 'I am a playwright; Miss Mooney is a producer. We don't speak the same language. If there are any revisions to be made in my play I will do them myself.'

In his curtain speech Brendan was, to say the least, ambiguous. After thanking Alan Simpson and Carolyn Swift for the first production, he went on to say, 'People must often have wondered how it feels to have a play produced by the Abbey Theatre. It feels like you think it would feel.' He went off to the theatre club with some members of the cast, and my wife and I went home to wait for the reviews – quite unknown to Brendan, I should add.

Apparently the critics brought their *Observers* instead of their football boots to the Abbey production. 'The play had vastly improved' or 'I forecast that there is a chance that at a later time somebody somewhere else will say that this man is brilliant and I will say then that we might have another O'Casey in our midst, or is it mist – anyway I mean it to be Celtic anyway.' I saw four productions of *The Quare Fella* and the only difference was three producer's names, and only one of those was in any way Celtic. I wouldn't like anybody to think that I have in any way quoted the critics of Ireland in what I've said. All I wanted to do was give an idea of what they mean – nothing.

12

'Whether you be cook's son
Earl's son or duke's son
Not one penny goes past the tombstone's Brink
So join the chorus
There's life before us
When you put your true trust in drink.'

AN FILE, BRENDÁIN O BEACÁIN.

⚜⚜⚜⚜⚜⚜⚜⚜⚜⚜⚜⚜⚜⚜⚜⚜⚜⚜⚜⚜⚜⚜

THE 'SILENCE AND CUNNING' BIT went down alright with
Brendan, but the 'exile' part didn't seem to suit him at all.
If box-office receipts were not too healthy-looking he would
hop across the pond and sing at a cinema queue in Leicester
Square, or jump on the stage in the middle of a performance. Anything for publicity, and Barnum had nothing
to teach Brendan. Somebody has knocked the British press
boys because they 'plied him with drink'. 'They were un-
scrupulous', it was said. Well, only the fairly big boys are
let loose by Fleet Street with money to spend like that, and
I can only say that people like Dave Nathan and Sam
Bestic spent more time in keeping Brendan sober than they
did money in knocking him drunk. He got what he wanted
– people to attend his play. But he never had any intention
of making 'The Irish Emigrant' his theme-song. Dublin was
the only *country* in the world for him.

Dr Johnson said that 'the Irish were a great race who
never spoke well of each other'. Living in Ireland, my

trouble was that nobody ever spoke about me at all, and, although it may be terrible to be ignored, to be ignored as somebody's brother is, I assure you, ten times worse.

From my 'book of bedtime quotes' (Brendan always maintained I possessed one) I learned that the good Doctor had also made some remark about the 'best prospect in Scotland being the High Road to London'. Wanting to prove this for myself, I gave a chap five shillings at the North Wall docks and he let me sit in his ship all the way to Glasgow. 'And look after him,' he shouted to a steward on deck, 'he's Brendan's brother.' Anyway, I can say that Dr Johnson was perfectly correct.

We made a programme, Hamish Henderson, Sean O'Boyle, and I, entitled 'The Scots and Irish Balladmakers' and Jack Dillon, the producer, scheduled it for production on a Wednesday evening. To be famous is dangerous. 'I see that Brendan Behan's brother has had his name in the paper.' 'Well, would yeh believe it! and him comin' from a most respectable family! What is he up for, mam?' On the Thursday morning I met a man in a pub who wanted me to buy him a drink. 'That was a great programme yeh did last night,' he remarked. 'I'm sorry,' said I, 'but I missed it!' 'Missed it!' he exclaimed. 'Yeh missed yer own programme? How could yeh do that?' 'It was postponed because of Vaughan Williams' death, until next week.' Brendan laughed at that story and said, 'The pleasure was in the missin' of it. I marvel that the English could think whiskey sufficient payment for a earful of the griddly-goo accompanied on the pipes. "Pipes," as me granny used to say, "are not worth a light without tobacco." '

Alan Simpson took my play *Posterity be Damned!* to Dublin and presented it at the Gaiety Theatre. I was singing the theme-song in and out through the performance and I had, therefore, a fair view of the audience. Among the

'Legion of Mary' candleers there were cries of 'Blasphemy!' quite often, but since they were required by their faith to bow heads whenever the Lord's name was taken in vain, most of the outbursts were directed to their feet. At the final curtain the house was wild, people even tried to get at me – but some gentlemen of foresight had provided me with the Irish playwright's best form of defence: a moat in the shape of a fine wide orchestra pit. Since the noun 'jazes' is common in Ireland as adjective and adverb too, not to mention the verb 'to jazes a man', I knew that the main objections of the Holy Willies were social and political, so I said, 'When you people couldn't keep me off the streets during the unemployed marches I'm damned sure you're not going to do it when I'm paying for the theatre.'

Brendan leaned from a box right over my head and shouted, 'That's it, Dom. Give it to the bastards! Up the Republic!' We drank together after and I was pleased that he had so reacted. Sometime later, however, other people remembered him to have shouted, 'Take it off, yeh bastard! Up the Republic!' The notices (when the critics had made their point about blasphemy) were mixed. I met one of the boys later at *The Hostage* and seeing him laugh his head silly in the bar, I asked, 'Did yeh not mind the blasphemy?' 'Oh,' he replied, 'they'd never let it into Ireland.' My brother speaks about such hypocrisy in his book *Brendan Behan's Island*.

'They will go to London,' he writes, 'and attend a play of mine or Sean O'Casey's, and they will inform all the English people that, of course, to really understand this play you've got to come from Dublin. Back home they will adopt either the straightforward outraged indignation of the censor and say: "We think this is a disgusting and immoral play," or they will say, as they have said about me, that I write to please English audiences. . . .' While speaking about not being able to procure a copy of Plato's *Symposium* because a bookseller was practising do-it-yourself censorship and had taken the book off the shelves. 'We saw a slight run on it, and the same sort of people looking for it, so we just took it out of circulation ourselves. After all, we don't have to be made decent-minded by Act of the Dail. We have our own way of detecting smut, no matter how ancient!'

When *The Hostage* arrived in London, it came like a rocket. Superlatives were at a premium, and you could have sold clichés for tenpence a bag. Was it anti-theatre, or uncle theatre? Everyone but Brendan was concerned about the label. He didn't give a damn, because the notices were good. It had followed hard on the heels of his book *Borstal Boy*, and Joan Littlewood's version of Brendan's English translation was enough to frighten the lives out of every bishop in Ireland. It was more than exciting. It was urgent, vital theatre. It left you, as Louis McNeice said when we saw it at the Wyndham's, 'like a damp rag, drained'. And yet I could see around that time sure signs that Brendan was departing from a position of strength to one of weakness. He was beginning to want to be liked. The applause was becoming a drug without which he wouldn't carry on. To translate his play from the Irish is a good thing to do, but to forget what he had written to Mr Blythe was in a writer a sign of decline.

While *The Hostage* was running at the Wyndham's, John Ryan, together with Alan Simpson, brought *Posterity be Damned!* to London, where it opened after a wrestling match (the next night I mean) at the Metropolitan Theatre, Edgware Road. Brendan came to a rehearsal, waited until there were enough press men around him, and shouted, 'Rubbish! There were no murderers in the IRA!' which translated into newspaper English means simply, 'Rubbish!' Bernard Levin and Milton Shulman saw, I think, what I was trying to do, and I thank them for that. And because Brendan only awoke from his seat in the stalls as the Press arrived to hear his remark, I like to think he was drunk on that occasion. Anyway, we broke a record: we were the only brothers to have plays running in London simultaneously for more than two hundred years. Oh, and I shouldn't forget, William Saroyan sent me a telegram in which he thanked me for '. . . a large slice of life'.

Even by his own standards Brendan was now drinking to excess. No more than I or most of my friends drink, maybe, but a lethal amount for anybody suffering from diabetes. 'Poor Bren,' Ma used to say when he was first released from prison, 'couldn't face grease. Ah no! Give him the salads and a bit of ham. Takes after me, yeh see, nothin' greasy.' He went to Paris with Theatre Workshop for a festival, and when he returned I went to see him in the Middlesex Hospital. I don't know what he heard about himself there, but when I met him later at Duncan Melvin's London flat I could have cried for the man I knew.

Duncan had phoned me around three in the morning, and in desperation asked for help with Brendan, who had become quite unmanageable. When I got there first he didn't know who I was from Adam, then he said simply, 'Dom, you'll get me a drink, won't yeh?' Duncan, out on his feet from a prolonged bout of tackling Brendan, went to bed, and I rang Max Sylvester, a friend of ours. Max arrived with a thimbleful of whiskey in a bottle laced with water, and Brendan was happy. On the following morning Brendan had to appear in Bow Street Court to answer a charge of being drunk and disorderly and Max drove him there. With what appeared to me to be a great effort he was jovial and verbose. They fined him about ten shillings and after reminding the judge that he had previous convictions not mentioned by the constable in evidence, he got into

Max's car and they drove to London Airport with my brother Sean. I followed behind by taxi – until I worried so much about the meter I asked the cab-driver to drop me off.

On the way to the airport he saw a regiment of horse and shouted 'Bollocks!' at them, and the greeting was mistaken for 'an old Irish war-cry' by the evening Press. I think it was at the airport that Max saw how really gentle he could be with children. A couple of boys approached as Brendan sat waiting for the plane and requested his autograph. 'Tell me,' asked my brother, 'how did yeh know who I was?' One of the lads told him how they had followed him from the court by taxi and, quite pleased and astonished that young folk should care so much he said, 'But it must have cost a bomb.' They told him it had cost around three quid. 'Sean,' said Brendan, 'for God's sake give these chisslers their money.' That incident made the trip to London worth while.

Lenny Bruce says that there are certain diseases to have and not have. Sympathy for cancer, disgust for tuberculosis. Recurring headaches are *au fait*, but people suffering from shingles are ill-bred. Brendan's disease was reflected in symptoms of sleepiness and incoherence. I've known common or garden drunks to look just like that – I'm not suggesting, of course, that people mistook them for diabetics. It did appear, however, that Brendan was driving himself into the ground by over-addiction to the hard tack, especially in view of his contention that as it had nothing to do with people they should mind their own business. He would neither confirm nor deny.

Sean O'Casey wrote to me: '. . . Ireland is not so well off for writers that she can afford to do without Brendan. Can you do nothing about his drinking? And you yourself, my young friend.' Dear sweet, lovely O'Casey, wouldn't any one of us have cut off our arms to do what you ask? Even had it done any good for himself it would have been a most special person, the one who could stop Brendan doing anything. Des McNamara spoke to him, so did Joe McGill. Rory Childers, his doctor, talked to him. But Brendan didn't need a cure for alcoholism. He was fond of a jar. We all are, because we're civilised folk who believe that 'Ireland sober is Ireland stiff', as James Joyce would say.

I was waiting in the Bailey Restaurant, where John Ryan and I had a luncheon appointment, when George Lalor, a member of the Old Guard Republicans, said to me, 'He never swore in front of my Molly. Him who could use bad language like a trooper. She thought he was the most gentle man. Which of course, he was.' For a moment I was stunned. George spoke of the dead. Then over his shoulder he greeted Ryan coming in the door, and as I looked up I saw Brendan sitting in the corner asleep.

'Is he often like that, John?' I asked. Ryan looked from me to my brother and replied, 'He's ill, Dom, and I don't believe it's the drink.' He asked me to accompany him upstairs to the dining-room and Brendan said sullenly from his seat, 'And am I not invited for lunch?' John smiled at me and assured my brother, 'Brendan, you can have as much lunch as you like. You can have the house, if it should please you.' Ryan and I discussed a new show we were planning at the Gate Theatre and suddenly John said to me, 'Why don't we do a play about the Catacombs?' I liked the idea of bringing the Ginger Man, McNamara, Brendan, and many more folk like Donleavy from 13a Fitzwilliam Place back to life from the past we'd lived together. It came to nothing, however, because Brendan announced to the Press on the following week that this would be the subject of his next play, only he would call it *Richard's Cork Leg*.

When we had eaten I took Brendan to the corner of

Anglsey Road, where he lived. He refused to go any farther than the bridge itself, however, and ordered the taxi-driver to head back to town. 'There's a party at Podmore's place tonight, I'd like to go,' and he added, 'you can come if you wish.'

I know what Wilde meant to convey when he made a man and the picture of a man. Podmore hadn't changed. Like a lord he sat among his serfs. A benevolent lord, but a lord nevertheless. He simply oozed old times and the older the times, the greater he oozed. And he called me Dom. I objected to his use of my brother as a star attraction for his student disciples. More than that, I objected to his use of my name in affection. What I objected to more than anything, I think, was Podmore.

A banjo-player sat on a table playing one-string variants of one-tone melodies on one string and Podmore explained that this was ethnic music. Around the feet of the bandore delinquent, people, who didn't know better, sighed. I don't think I've ever known anything more undignified than the spectacle of this unfortunate, stupid man being hawked as quaint. Though at least he was doing whatever he was doing for a reason, a few jars maybe and a night's lodging. When Podmore called on me to sing I was fit to burst. 'I will,' I said, 'for my fee!' Brendan stirred up from his chair and shouted, 'Yeh Third Programme yahoo! Yeh BBC lackey! Who the hell wants yeh to sing! I'll sing songs yeh never heard tell of.' Then he commenced to sing the lovely 'Sliab na mBan' and I was sorry I didn't put my anger where I'd so often left my pride. The times I'd heard him thrill a company with that same song. Now his voice was quite unable to fulfil his desire. After a verse he stopped, and I slipped away.

13

'Sad is the theme and the muse of my story
Gone are the days of the snug and it's glory
Dark are the hours that are hovering o'er me
Down in the Village we tarried too long.'

PEADER KEARNEY

✤✤✤✤✤✤✤✤✤✤✤✤✤✤✤✤✤✤✤✤✤✤✤✤✤✤

ERIC EWENS OF BBC SCRIPTS rang me one day and said that the
Corporation were planning a series to be entitled 'Plays from
the Fifties'. Would I like to do *The Hostage* together with
H. A. L. Craig? It wasn't all that simple. Firstly I didn't want
to get tied up in any of Brendan's business, and secondly
my brother and I were not what one might describe as well
met by literature, or drama, or what they have thought of
calling *The Hostage*. Besides, since the publication of my
book *Teems of Times and Happy Returns*, Brendan had been
telling folk that I was interfering in his memories. And yet
The Hostage had a strange fascination for me, it was like a
huge character-making factory. People came in one door
as ponces and puffs and with a wave of a pen he turned them
to Junos and Fluthers. 'A whore with a heart of gold,' Pat,
the brothel-keeper, talks about, and his 'blaspheming'
attack on hypocrisy took on a holiness that the Salvation
Army and The Legion of Mary would not be endowed with
if somebody was to offer them all ringside seats for a repeat
performance of the crucifixion. I said I'd work on the play,
then I set about seeing Brendan.

I missed him two or three times in a matter of a couple of

days, and maybe just as well, because, according to what some folks were saying, he wasn't, at the moment, well disposed towards me. But I'd been hearing stories like this for a long time, and they were always exaggerated accounts of rhetorical swear-bashing. 'The dirty rotten so and so! If I had him this minit, be the livin' jazes I'd . . .' And whoever happened to be on the make for a few quid at the time would report that I had done this, that, or the other. Indeed I met one man for the first time, a few days after his death, who had been 'letting Brendan in' on the 'inside' story of my attitude to his work. What I had said about his work, in the mind of this gentleman, was not to Brendan very complimentary. My brother, I'm sure, would have disregarded most of the man, and his conversation, as rubbish, but some would stick; to inspire after-dinner conversational invective if nothing else. If the gentleman concerned happens to be reading this passage at the moment I would like him to understand that Jack London had compassion for the filth left over by God after the creation of the scab. I forgive you, after I forgive the scab.

Brendan came straight up to me in the ML Club in Little Portland Street and attacked me for criticising his granny. I told him the BBC wanted me to adapt *The Hostage* for radio. Why hadn't I sent him a copy of my book? I asked why he never let me have one of his. Would he like me to do the play or not? His granny was no rack-renter. Maybe he would like something to eat. He observed that McNeice was a friend of Kavanagh's. McNeice smiled. I wouldn't do *The Hostage* unless he would like me to do it. I was to see Gerry Raffles of Theatre Workshop and say he OK'd it. It was agreed, then? It was. Would he wait till Sean came? Did I not trust him? I didn't. Alright, he'd say it in front of Sean.

If I did *The Hostage* I would do myself grave harm. He was

only giving me good advice. Why should it harm me? People would say I was up on his back. They were saying that already. He never said it! Arnold Wesker having refused BBC permission to do his trilogy would agree if I adapted the plays. A good boy Wesker. Would people say I was up on *his* back? Alright, so he'd said yes, did I have to keep on? Here was Sean, I wanted *him* to hear. He wanted to know if Sean had read what I'd been saying about his granny. I thought he hadn't read the book? He'd more to do with his time. I'd send him the copy he'd requested. I was to stuff it – as high as Gilderoy!

Reviewing the radio adaptation of *The Hostage* in *The Listener*, Ian Rodger said: 'I saw it on the stage where it had been given very lavish treatment and I was therefore surprised to find some excellent dialogue and a clear plot emerging . . . the temptation to make an Irish joke of the whole thing, in order to give West End audiences what they need from Ireland, overcame the author's more serious preoccupations with the folly of sham militarism, the waste of executions of young men and a belief in the resurrection of any good man.' We had made a point, Craig and I and the man who produced it, H. B. Fortuin.

14

'Wrap the green flag round me boys
To die were far more sweet
With Erin's noble emblem boys
To be my winding sheet
In life I longed to see it wave
And follow where it led
But now my eyes grow dim — my hand
Would grasp its last bright shred.'

***

'BUT OH I EH, OH YES. There's a place outside, outside Toronto – would yis shut up for a minit? There's a place outside Toronto, Ontario. And I was in hospital there, with a guy called Dr . . . He'd three Irish nurses – I should say Catholic nurses. He was Jewish. And, there's another doctor in this fucking lark with me, and . . . I'd many experiences of Canada. Lot of Canadians think I hate Canada. I don't hate – I won't say I don't hate anybody, say well, I make certain exceptions. But very few people do I really dislike. There's a place in Ontario where they invited a family from Europe; not from Eastern Europe; not from the Stalin Alley – the Stalin Alley might have a funny name to you. But calling it the Stalin Alley is no funnier than calling it – what d'ye call that main street in Toronto? Young Street, that's right. But what d'ye call Spodina where yeh get the hungry guys? Well, I saw Stalin Alley, and it wasn't as bad as Spodina. I'll

tell yeh that. I mean I, one of the worst crimes I com-
mitted on the middle class of . . . on the bourgeois of
Canada was that I went along a big . . . I got from the
O'Keefe Centre in Toronto. . . . I got four hundred and
I . . .'

The foregoing is a complete passage from a tape made by
Brendan in the summer of 1962. He wasn't drunk, nor have
I edited his words in any way. I publish it here because
people will ask why I have not mentioned *Brendan Behan's*
New York. Paul Hogarth's drawings are excellent, but I
would refer you to the widow of a man killed in the Boer
War when on being asked to accept his posthumous decora-
tion she replied, 'I know not if he might think he worthy
of the medal or the medal worthy of he.' George Bernard
Shaw, on a visit to New York, remarked, 'I had better be
careful lest I should want to change my mind for the
microphone is a fearfully faithful instrument.' Dead men
tell plenty of tales but a tape-recorder will never change its
mind.

'Good to see yeh back,' said Long Paddy Kelly as I walked
into the *Harbour Lights Bar*. 'Aye,' agreed Charlie Joe
Gorman. 'Thought maybe yeh'd grown too high and
mighty with yer pop records and all that.' Kelly put his
hand to his brow and pleaded, 'For the love of God, Charlie
Joe Gorman, don't mention that song in this respectable
public house. Me daughters have me absolutely murdered
with it!' Rory laughed and said, 'It's the title amuses me,
"Liverpool Lou". Had the other fella known that one of his
would say a good word about Liverpool he'd have gone
clean off his head.' 'Called it a desert in the middle of an
oasis,' remarked Eddie Connell.

'He was the one for the songs,' Dick Timmons said. 'You
couldn't hold a candle to him, Dominic; could he, Paddy?'
'Well,' said Kelly, 'in the old days. But not lately. Very poor

towards the end. Isn't that right, Charlie?' 'See him in the snug there,' Charlie explained, 'and there'd be the most abominable caterwallin' and Brendan would just sit and put up with it. Could do nothin' else, of course.'

'Did he come in a lot, then?' I asked the company. 'Only towards the end,' replied Kelly, 'about the last eight months.' 'About that,' agreed Charlie. 'Up till then he'd been leeched off by the biggest shower of touchers in the city. Eddie Whelan brought him back with Finnegan.' 'Oh,' said Paddy Kelly sadly, 'it's a terrible pity Whelan and Finnegan couldn't have got him earlier. I'm sure we could have done somethin' anyway. Still, he came back to his own and that's what's important.'

Charlie Joe ordered another drink and said confidentially, 'He called me down into that snug one day and said, "Charlie, I want to talk to yeh, and I don't want yeh to interrupt me till I finish what I have to say." "Fire away, Brendan," said I. "When I die, Charlie, I want yeh to make sure that I get the flag." "Now for God's sake, Brendan, will yeh stop talkin' of dyin', sure yeh'll see us all down." "Charlie," he said, "you and I and Kelly have been a long time together, so don't let us kid ourselves. I'm for the high jump and that's that. I want yeh to make sure that when I die it's your flag, the flag of the Republic, no Staters flag that goes round me." "I will, Brendan. I'll put the flag that wrapped Danny Conroy and many another good man around yeh, and I'll see to that meself." And I did, Dominic, and we took the funeral over from the toffs and buried Brendan as he would have wanted. One of his own with his own.' 'Yes,' Kelly repeated, 'he came back to his own.'

Kelly ordered me to sing and I did so. We sang every rebel song in the book and relived ten hundred rebel funerals and commemorations and every song I sang was a song that Brendan sung and my own ones were not welcome, although I had been called upon to sing to get the company away from things sad, but even now Brendan wouldn't let us alone and at the end of 'Sliab na mBan' Kelly said:

'In the last week before he went to the hospital he was sittin' in the snug and he not able to move. A toff of an oulwan comes in.' 'An overdressed bitch,' said Charlie. Kelly went on, 'She was ready to needle Brendan, and she says, "Why don't you write a book?"' Charlie butted in. ' "But," said Brendan, "I've written books, and plays as well."' Kelly took over. ' "I mean," she said, "a good book."' 'Oh,' agreed Charlie with Kelly's expression, 'a sarcastic oul gett!' Kelly continued as though he'd never been interrupted. Paddy is like that. ' "Well, missus," said Brendan . . .' Charlie rubbed his hands vigorously in anticipation. 'Wait,' he said, 'wait'll yeh hear how he choked off this oul whore.' Kelly chose his words carefully. It was the sort of story could easily come out the wrong way in the telling. ' "I have your number, now," he said to this one – very cool, oh but Brendan could play it very cool. "There's the rich people at the top with money and no manners. There's the poor at the bottom with manners and no money. You, missus, belong to that gang in the middle who have neither money nor manners."'

15

'Come boosers hearty and join the party
And see the cares of this wide world sink
As people pour us the only chorus
That we should put our true trust in drink.'

REPRINTED FROM 'LIFE' MAGAZINE

I'LL NEVER FORGET THE MORNING, afternoon, and evening of
the day we buried Brendan – it was the first time in my
company he didn't monopolise the conversation, though,
come to think of it, he did, for all the talk was about him
or his extraordinary exploits. Even at the graveside his
history stalked before us as live as a policeman he had shot
at in 1942 who whispered to me, 'A lot of IRA men here
don't like me because I got Brendan a stretch one time, but
let me tell them that had I returned the fire that time I
could have shot him dead, your brother owes his life to
me,' and Brendan never flinched a smile-muscle, for they
were beginning to throw clay in on top of him.

The only funeral like it took place in 1904, when Mr
Patrick Dignam was laid to rest in the same Glasnevin
Cemetery, but we won't count that one since it only
happened inside the covers of Mr Joyce's *Ulysses*. There
were poets and peasants, painters and publicans, 'the world
and his wife', as Dean Swift would say, had gathered in the
hope that Brendan would prove it all a lie and rise from the
box like Finnegan, to take them all away from the cold
graveyard and out into the bright morning sunshine for

one last drink. But even more wonderful was the spectacle of more than a thousand working-class folk who had taken a day off to say goodbye – one day, one-fifth of their whole week's wages, no mean sacrifice.

Everything must have a beginning, a middle, and an end, except Brendan Behan's life – it had no beginning, unless you call spending youth with old lags and adolescence with mature political prisoners a childhood. He didn't play for long under the street-lamp with us, for at the age of six he had joined the ranks of the young IRA and by the very hour of his sixteenth birthday he was already in Walton Jail starting his first stretch. He was twenty-three years of age before they let him loose on the world, a man-boy with his first toy – freedom. Seeing life for the first time he grabbed everything with both hands and set about the job of living as an historian tackles the business of compressing centuries.

That, then, was the time people call 'formative years' when trying to describe what it was that made a man turn out as he did in later life. They might as well have tried to tell the time by a sundial in the middle of the night, for Brendan's 'formative years' were being lived longing for a longer look at 'That little tent of blue which prisoners call the sky' while the literary analysts were sailing down the Thames on their first most dangerous voyage, the mad manly mission of winning the Oxford boat race. 'A drunk', they called him, as they stottered from their typewriters and staggered into the press club for one large glass of brandy on credit – because their month's salary was already in hock to the man behind the bar. They had written the 'Wild One's' obituary five years before and now all they had to do was change the age from thirty-six to forty-one – easy for men who think that all 'drunks' die from diabetes and all alcoholics are Brendan Behans. More alcoholics and drunks left that cemetery than stayed behind, and the population of Glasnevin is great indeed.

Brendan's chief enemy was his ability to forgive. In *The Quare Fellow* he finds time to talk of warders who are not 'too bad' or, in prisons elsewhere, governors who 'detest' what they are doing when they wash their hands after greeting the hangman.

Because they had not been able to see *The Hostage* in its original Gaelic form people who cared thought that 'Brendan had not developed as a playwright' – it was 'too loose', 'the structure indecisive', 'the hallmark of the dramatist was just not there'. They couldn't know how it had been mutilated by folk who couldn't stick to the job they know best – putting on and acting in plays. It wasn't world praise for *The Hostage* that made Brendan go off the deep end; on the contrary, it was the sadness of being left with only the shadow of a magnificent play. And yet one would need the cast-iron will of a Shaw, a Beckett, or an O'Casey to protect one's art from such people who think that writers are merely puppets at the end of their Punch and Judy Theatre strings. Poor Brendan, he must have been heartbroken.

'I wasn't heartbroken,' he's saying somewhere. 'I didn't care. I didn't give a damn just so long as I didn't have to paint walls, or dig trenches, or die for Ireland. This art you talk of is only a figment of your serious imagination. Don't write about me as though I was some sort of culture vulture with no other ambition but that of dying in a museum to be surrounded by old women and quaint men who think there's nothing better in life than drying their eyes through sobbing for dear dead Shakespeare. Get off that stunt and tell them about me. That's the subject they've asked you to cover.'

Alright, then, about Brendan. There was the time we

walked behind my first girl friend's funeral – I don't want you to think I bury all my girl friends. 'Cry,' he ordered.

'I don't feel like crying – Brendan, I didn't care that much. It would be hypocrisy.'

'If you can't be a simple thing like a hypocrite for no more than half an hour then you're not much of a brother. Will you not shed even a few tears to encourage the relatives to buy a drink?'

I cried and they didn't buy a drink and Brendan made a note of all the other daughters' names to be sure that he mightn't be caught in the same predicament himself.

He enjoyed other people's funerals because they couldn't do that for themselves, but when some people talk about him having a death wish they must be joking. Brendan wanted to live very much and I'm sure he would never have allowed us to take him to the cemetery at all had it not been for the fact that he was about to entertain his largest personal audience. As he said himself about publicity, 'There's no such thing as bad publicity except your own obituary.'

Brendan's funeral (what a strange sound that has) lacked one ingredient – the essential Behan. Oh, he was at it right enough, but strangely silent. Probably because there was no one there able to see the funny side of the affair, they were upset and he was sad to see them so, and he was unable to do anything to cheer them up. Maybe they all had their private memories, like the time he went into a hock shop to pawn his typewriter and then handed the money to a poor woman trying to get money for a meal on a bundle of rags. Or when he marched twelve frozen Dubliners into a tailor's one Christmas and ordered one dozen overcoats. The countless people he had saved from being evicted by paying their arrears of rent. They might have come just because they remembered a man who walked into their lives, bought a round of drinks, sang a song or two, and left them with hope. Why they came doesn't really matter, but I'm sure of one thing, they didn't attend his funeral to pay respect to 'a brain hit by a bottle'.

There are in this world a few literatured people and they are called writers. And when a man can talk nearly as well as Oscar Wilde he would be bound to ask, 'Why wear my fingers to the bone on a typewriter?' There are, of course, exceptions like Shaw, but then he had a political job in hand as much as a literary one. 'What was the message of your play, Mr Behan?' somebody asked after the first night of *The Hostage*. 'Message? Message?' said Brendan, 'what the hell do you think I am, a bloody postman?'

There is no point in conjecturing on how Brendan would have developed had he been left alone and not been eaten alive by the pagan human lions into whose den he had been thrown by people who would have been terrified had he turned into a Brecht. Any chance of that is all over now. For the layabouts and ponces who bled him white I have no sympathy in knowing that they now have to go back to working for a living. For the journalists who avoided sensationalism in their death notices – and they were in the majority – I thank them for remembering 'The Laughing Boy' as he was at other times.